Children's WARD

BASED ON GRANADA TV's DRAMA SERIES

Devised by Paul Abbott and Kay Mellor,
and written by Paul Abbott, Kay Mellor
and John Chambers
Edited by Lawrence Till

Heinemann Educational,
a division of Heinemann Educational Books Ltd,
Halley Court, Jordan Hill, Oxford OX2 8EJ

OXFORD LONDON EDINBURGH MADRID ATHENS BOLOGNA PARIS
MELBOURNE SYDNEY AUCKLAND SINGAPORE TOKYO IBADAN NAIROBI
HARARE GABORONE PORTSMOUTH NH (USA)

First published in the *Heinemann Plays* series by Heinemann Educational
1992.

A catalogue record for this book is available from the British Library on
request.

ISBN 435 23285 1

Cover design by Keith Pointing
Designed by Jeffrey White Creative Associates
Typeset by Taurus Graphics, Abingdon, Oxon.
Printed by Clays Ltd, St Ives plc

Contents

Introduction

With an average of 5.8 million viewers, Granada Television's *Children's Ward* is one of the most popular children's programmes on television. It has won several awards, including the prestigious New York Television and Film Silver Award in 1990, and has been applauded for its realism. The scripts in this book are the first six episodes of the third series, which was first broadcast between October 1990 and January 1991.

Children's Ward is a drama series set in the children's ward of a northern hospital – South Park General, or Sparkies as it is affectionately known. The strength of the series comes from the fact that children handle illness in a completely different, and often much more successful, way to adults.

Under the umbrella of the children's ward, there is a cross section of personalities and ages, all often bored and desperate for fresh air – a prime breeding ground for new friendships, jealousies and gossip.

Children's Ward deals with a range of issues in a thought-provoking and entertaining way which can be used to stimulate discussion, writing and drama. The follow-up questions and activities for each episode at the end of the book provide a basis for this classroom work. They are addressed to the student, but clearly rely on the teacher's judgement as to which areas of enquiry best suit a particular group.

In preparing the episodes for inclusion in this book, I have modified some of the film and studio directions to allow the episodes to be read with the least confusion or interruption. I have also rearranged some of the scenes to avoid constant shifts of focus, which are easily understood on television but can often confuse a reader.

However, the scripts are still recognisably television plays, and so offer a good opportunity for studying the medium as well as the characters, plots and issues.

For example, as television plays are conceived visually, it would be useful and interesting to discuss where and how scenes should be shot before reading them. This is particularly so with the first episode, which, like all first episodes, moves around fairly rapidly to introduce characters and plot lines. (Before reading the first episode it would also be useful to read the notes on existing characters from previous series.)

It is also useful to work out which scenes were recorded on a studio set and which needed filming on location. To help planning internal scenes, simplified ground plans of the sets themselves are provided at the end of the book.

Their origins in television also mean that these scripts are particularly suitable for production on video. (Please note that the copyright holder, Granada Television, would need to be consulted in advance about any plan to record.)

There is also an opportunity to explore the way in which scripts for on-going television series are written. The series is planned out in advance as a set of storylines for all the episodes. The writers then write to these storylines, referring to notes on the characters which help to ensure continuity between series and episodes.

This book contains the storyline for Episode One for comparison with the actual script. It also has notes which provide background on characters from the first two series. Both provide useful guidelines for students scripting additional scenes or writing their own storylines.

Finally, a glossary at the end of the book provides definitions and explanations of the medical and hospital terms encountered in the scripts. There are relatively few, and most will be well known, but the glossary ensures that unknown words do not spoil the flow and enjoyment of reading the text.

Lawrence Till

Note on the Writers

Kay Mellor (Episodes One and Two)

Studied drama at Bretton Hall College. Her stage plays include *Paul, Scenes from Engles, Climbing Out, A Question of No!, Mother of Mine, Mates*, and *In all Innocence*.

In 1985 she became a script editor for Granada Television working on *Albion Market* and *Coronation Street*. In 1987 she was commissioned to write *Living Doll* for the Dramarama series and in 1988 co-devised *Children's Ward* with Paul Abbott. Her one-hour drama for Yorkshire TV in 1988, *Place of Safety*, won an Emmy award and was nominated for the coveted Prix Italia prize. Since 1989 she has both devised and written *Families* for Granada.

Paul Abbott (Episodes Three and Four)

Started writing at the age of fourteen, initially selling short stories to national magazines, and won the Frederick Milne Award at seventeen.

In 1980, he started writing radio plays for BBC Radio 4 and the World Service, including *Jennifer, David and . . . who's Goliath?* and *Soldier Boy*. His plays for the theatre include *The Fall and Death of Willie Blob, Rats, Monkeys in the Sun, Amazing Grace* and *Binnin' It*.

He started working for television in 1984 as a writer on *Coronation Street*, and co-created *Children's Ward* with Kay Mellor in 1988 in response to what they saw as a need for new hard-hitting and funny children's drama.

John Chambers (Episodes Five and Six)

Before becoming a professional writer in 1984, John had a number of jobs including labourer, telephone engineer, and laboratory technician in a blood bank! He also worked as a social and community worker for twelve years.

He has written a number of plays for theatre, including *Two Wheel Tricycle, Stiff Stuff* and *Tales of King Arthur*. For television he has been a writer on *Emmerdale Farm, Eastenders, Maths is Fun*, and Dramarama as well as *Children's Ward* and several thirty-minute plays for BBC2.

List of Characters

Episodes One to Six

Patients	*Years Old*
Lee Jones	15
James Boyce	11
Bryony Schaffer	14
Darren Walsh	13
Danny Phillips	10
Cal Spicer	16
Lucy Clarkson	6
Rowena Easson	8
Philip Dean	9
Hannah Bevans	3
Jack Bevans	6 months old

Staff

Dr Kieran Gallagher
Dr Charlotte Woods
Sister Diane Meadows
Nurse Sandra Mitchell
Auxillary Nurse Mags
Student Nurse Gary Miller
Student Nurse Katie Grahams
Keely Johnson, play worker
Nurse John Langdon (renal unit)
Dr Kahn, neurologist
Dr Tanya Davies, casualty officer
Jack Crossley, trolleyman
Steve Bailey, social worker
Dr Bev Morris, food allergy specialist

Physiotherapist
Hospital radio DJ
Ambulance man
Neurology technician
Radiologist

Relatives, visitors and others

Mrs Carol Jones
Mr Eddie Jones
Marcus Jones
Mrs Gail Bevans
Billy Ryan
Ben Rowlingson
Mr Phillips
Mrs Phillips
Mr Schaeffer
Mrs Schaeffer
Mr Appleyard
Newsagent
Esther, Jack Bevans' grandma
Frances, Eddie Jones' girlfriend
Mr Starkey, team coach
Mr Harries, referee

(Not all appear in each episode. See the separate episode
character lists for details.)

Episode One

Patients
Lee
James
Bryony
Darren
Danny
Cal
Lucy

Staff
Dr Gallagher
Dr Woods
Sister Meadows
Nurse Mitchell
Nurse Mags
Nurse Miller
Nurse Grahams
Keely
Nurse Langdon
Dr Davies
Jack Crossley
Ambulance man

Relatives etc
Mrs Jones
Ben
Mr Appleyard

Episode Two

Patients
Lee
James
Bryony
Darren
Danny
Cal
Lucy
Philip

Staff
Dr Gallagher
Dr Woods
Sister Meadows
Nurse Mitchell
Nurse Mags
Nurse Grahams
Keely
Nurse Langdon
Steve

Relatives etc
Mrs Jones
Mr Jones
Marcus
Ben
Mr Phillips
Mrs Phillips

Episode Three

Patients
Lee
James
Bryony
Darren
Danny
Cal
Lucy
Rowena
Philip
Jack Bevans

Staff

Dr Gallagher
Dr Woods
Sister Meadows
Nurse Mitchell
Nurse Mags
Nurse Grahams
Keely
Nurse Langdon
Dr Kahn
Dr Davies
Jack Crossley
Dr Morris
DJ

Relatives etc

Mrs Bevans
Billy Ryan
Mrs Phillips
Newsagent

Episode Four

Patients
Lee
James
Bryony
Darren
Danny
Cal
Rowena
Philip
Hannah
Jack Bevans

Staff

Dr Gallagher
Dr Woods
Sister Meadows
Nurse Mitchell
Nurse Mags
Nurse Grahams
Keely
Nurse Langdon
Physiotherapist
Neurology technician

Relatives etc

Mrs Jones
Mr Jones
Mrs Bevans
Mrs Phillips
Esther
Frances

Episode Five

Patients
Lee
James
Bryony
Darren
Danny
Cal
Lucy
Rowena
Philip
Jack Bevans

Staff

Dr Gallagher
Dr Woods
Sister Meadows
Nurse Mitchell
Nurse Mags
Nurse Grahams
Keely
Nurse Langdon
Jack Crossley
Physiotherapist
DJ
Radiologist

Relatives etc

Mrs Bevans
Billy Ryan
Ben

Episode Six

Patients
Lee
James
Bryony
Darren
Danny
Cal
Lucy
Rowena
Philip
Hannah
Jack Bevans

Staff

Dr Gallagher
Dr Woods
Sister Meadows
Nurse Mitchell
Nurse Mags
Nurse Grahams
Nurse Langdon

Relatives etc

Mrs Jones
Mrs Bevans
Mr Schaeffer
Mrs Schaeffer
Mr Starkey
Mr Harries

Character Backgrounds

Patients

Bryony Schaeffer (14)

Bryony is coming to terms with a crippling disease – Rheumatoid Arthritis – and is in hospital for bed rest before treatment can properly begin. She has had a protected childhood with well-off middle-class parents, but is an independent girl with a strong sense of humour.

Rowena Easson (8)

An over-confident girl whose aspiration is to be a majorette. She constantly tells people 'how she nearly made it into the first team' and frequently plays her mini-cassio keyboard which she brought in with her. She is a witterer, and staff and patients alike are desperate for her to get her tonsils out just to give her tongue a rest. But no sooner is she back from theatre than she is wittering away again.

Lucy Clarkson (6)

Scalded her legs when she pulled a teapot over herself. When she leaves the children's ward, she will probably transfer to a specialist unit for skin grafts. She has an embarrassing habit – she still sucks a dummy at her late age, which suggests she is fairly insecure. When she remembers, she takes it out and hides it.

James Boyce (11)

James first appeared in the second series, newly diagnosed with diabetes. He found it difficult to cope at first, especially with the thought of regular self-injections, but has now adapted to his condition. He has been admitted for a reassessment, as he has grown a couple of inches over recent months and his treatment has to be adjusted accordingly.

Darren Walsh (13)

A very athletic, macho boy whose style has been cramped by developing very non-macho asthma. Forms a pair with James, mostly in thinking up mischief.

Staff

Dr Kieran Gallagher (26)

An easy-going, generous man with a sense of humour. Apparently laid back but on the ball as a doctor. Not keen on rules, and the senior medical establishment have long since given up trying to get him to dress conventionally as a doctor rather than in baggy T-shirts. Some other members of staff are not keen on his frayed-around-the-edges look and relaxed attitude.

Keely Johnson (17)

Keely was introduced in the first series as a mature street-wise fourteen-year-old, generally very confident and full of herself. She was admitted for hepatitis after her DIY tatoo became infected, and she then developed anorexia.
In the second series she planned to train as a nurse, but discovered that she was pregnant, which threatens these plans. She is still determined to take her nursery nurse exams, however, and meanwhile is working as a play volunteer on the

children's ward. The father of her child, Billy Ryan, wants them to settle down together as a family. Keely is not so sure and faces important decisions about her and the baby's future.

Billy Ryan (17)

An ex-patient of the ward who keeps in touch via Keely. He loves Keely more, he believes, than she loves him. He wants them to live together as a family.

Auxiliary Nurse Mags (52)

A mature auxiliary and the mainstay of everyday life on the children's ward. She is very experienced and has a lot to offer, although she can be rather intolerant on occasions. She has a sharp edge to her tongue but a genuine concern for the children in her care.

Sister Diane Meadows (25)

A young nursing sister who never hoped to achieve promotion so quickly. She has to struggle to prove her worth to people like Nurse Mitchell who imagines she would have made a better sister herself.

Dr Charlotte Woods (33)

A strong minded woman who decided at an early age that she wanted to be a doctor. Acidic at times, and known for her quick temper, she holds the long-term plan of moving into general practice.

Nurse Sandra Mitchell (32)

Awkwardly cold and officious, she is a nurse who wants to run everything by the book. Nevertheless, she is capable, and can run the ward without the intervention of superiors. She has no capacity for handling everyday emotions but she proves to be a warm and caring professional when the need arises.

Student Nurse Gary Miller (19)

Clumsy and awkward, Nurse Miller always seems to be in the wrong place at the wrong time. He desperately wants to be a good nurse but the harder he tries the worse he gets. If he does not shape up soon, he and Sister Meadows will need to have a serious talk about his career.

Jack Crossley (60)

The trolleyman who sells drinks and sweets around the hospital. He is aggressive, arrogant and self-important. Not really very nice to know, especially on the children's ward where he is treated with a justifiable lack of respect. But his bark is worse than his bite.

Steve Bailey (30)

Social worker attached to the children's ward of Sparkies. Always on call to advise on the non-medical care of patients.

Episode One
by Kay Mellor

Scene 1 *(External): Football pitch*

A football pitch, late in the afternoon. We see several pairs of soccer boots chasing after the football. One pair of boots is particularly skilled and we focus in on them as they lead the way to an imminent goal. We hear several shouts of 'Go on, stick it in', etc. We see the boots driving the ball towards the goal posts. We see another pair of boots running across the field into a tackle position. We see the young, aggressive, competitive face of Lee Jones as he is determined to see the ball home. As he nears the goal posts his face distorts into a picture of sheer agony. We hear the thud of a football boot hitting flesh. We see the offending foot as it goes into the young body of Lee Jones. The slow motion effect turns to reality as Lee falls to the ground. The whistle is blown and we hear boos from the opposition. We see the offender's face as a penalty is awarded. We see the referee's face as he sees Lee still on the ground. The referee, Mr Appleyard, goes over to Lee. Several shouts of 'scam' continue as we close up on the face of Lee.

Mr Appleyard   Are you all right lad . . . what's the matter? . . . Jones! Can you hear me?

Lee groans and we see he looks very ill. Some of the other lads have gathered round.

Mr Appleyard   Rowlingson!!!

Ben   Yes, sir?

Mr Appleyard   Get Mrs Crawley to ring for an ambulance.

Ben   Sir.

And Ben Rowlingson runs off in the direction of the school office.

Scene 2 *(External): High street/Ambulance*

An ambulance races through the streets, with blue lights flashing and sirens sounding; a car pulls into the side to let the ambulance pass. The ambulance team are working hard to make life easier for Lee. Mr Appleyard is by Lee's side. He has a pair of tracksuit bottoms on over his sports kit. Lee is groaning in pain. He is still dressed in his soccer kit.

Ambulance Man It's all right, Lee, we'll have you there in two minutes. You just hold on. Steady.

And we close up on Lee trying to do just that.

Scene 3 *(Internal): Corridor to casualty*

Lee's trolley is being pushed through the crash doors, with the ambulance driver, a nurse, and Mr Appleyard by Lee's side. Oxygen is being administered. The casualty doctor – Dr Tanya Davies – is wearing a white coat. She walks down the corridor to greet the approaching trolley as it is being wheeled towards the emergency treatment room.

Dr Davies Put him in emergency.

Scene 4 *(Internal): Casualty treatment room*

Dr Davies takes a blood sample and attaches a drip to Lee's arm. We see no change in reaction on Lee's face. The Doctor hands the phial of blood to the nurse.

Dr Davies As fast as you can please. Tell them I need it like yesterday.

The nurse dashes off with the phial of blood.

Dr Davies OK, Lee, show me again where it's hurting.

Lee points to his back and around his side.

Lee I feel sick.

Dr Davies gives him a bowl. We hear but do not

see him being sick.

Dr Davies Finished?

Lee nods his head and flops back down on the trolley exhausted.

Dr Davies You're doing fine. OK, let's go then.

We see Lee as his trolley is about to be wheeled out of the room heading off for the scan room.

Scene 5 *(External): Hospital gates*

Mrs Carol Jones (Lee's mother) runs into the hospital grounds. She looks anxious. She meets Jack Crossley the trolley-man wheeling his trolley down the corridor. Mrs Jones approaches from the opposite direction. Mrs Jones is in a panic and out of breath.

Mrs Jones Casualty?

Jack is aggressive and deliberately provocative:

Jack Is that a question or statement?

Mrs Jones is desperate.

Mrs Jones Casualty! Where is it?

Jack answers acidically.

Jack Round the corner, follow the green line.

And she's off. He shouts after her, sarcastically:)

Jack Thank you very much, Mr Crossley, for your time. If I'd have wanted to direct people I'd have joined the police force.

He goes off down the corridor, chuntering and imitating Mrs Jones.

Jack Casualty? No please, no thank you . . .

Scene 6 *(Internal): Scanner waiting area.*

A grim-faced Mr Appleyard, not quite sure what he should be doing, is in the waiting area near the scanner room. Mrs Jones arrives at the waiting area. Mr Appleyard, pleased to see Lee's mother at long last, stands to greet her.

Mrs Jones   They rang me at work. I got here as soon as I could. Where is he?

Mr Appleyard   They're just giving him a scan.

Mrs Jones   What happened?

Mr Appleyard   I've no idea; he took a kick on the field and just keeled over.

Scene 7 *(Internal): Scanner unit*

Dr Davies is assisting the staff in the scanner unit. Lee is undergoing an ultrasound scan of the abdomen area. We see what the Doctor sees, as the machine records Lee's body.

Dr Davies   And hold it there.

The scanner operator does just that. Dr Charlotte Woods enters.

Dr Davies   Take a look at this.

Dr Woods looks at the scanner picture.

Dr Woods   I haven't seen anything like that since Medical school. That's one for Mr Anderton, I think. Take him up to intensive care and book theatre.

Dr Davies wheels Lee out of the scanner unit. Mrs Jones leaps up. The trolley is wheeled away and Dr Wood's takes Mrs Jones aside.

Mrs Jones   Lee!!!

She turns to Dr Woods.

Mrs Jones   Is he all right?

Dr Woods   Are you his mother?

Mrs Jones   Yes, what's the matter with him?

Dr Woods   I'm afraid your son's kidney has taken quite a severe blow and we're just trying to assess how much damage has been done.

Mrs Jones   Oh! My god . . . what's going to happen to him?

Dr Woods	Most people have two kidneys Mrs Jones, but in Lee's case, he's only got one. The kidney on the right side hasn't developed properly.
Mrs Jones	But nobody's ever said anything like this to me before.
Dr Woods	Well unless he's had his kidney's x-rayed, there's no reason for anybody to know. The problem is that the renal artery on the left kidney is leaking.

Dr Davies returns, and extends her hand to Mrs Jones.

Dr Davies	Hello, I'm Dr Davies; I'm afraid your son's in quite a bit of pain at the moment and Mr Anderton would like to operate immediately. There's internal bleeding and we need to have a proper look to assess the damage, so if you would sign this consent form please, Mrs Jones.

Dr Davies hands her the form. Dr Woods hands her the pen and tries to reassure her.

Dr Woods	He's in safe hands. Mr Anderton is one of the top kidney surgeons in the country.

Scene 8 *(Internal): Children's ward*

Keely is drawing a picture for Lucy, who is sitting on her bed sucking her dummy.

Keely	And this is a gingerbread house, with a gingerbread chimney . . . are you listening?
Lucy	Why are you so fat?

She puts the dummy straight back in her mouth.

Keely	I'm not fat; I'm going to have a baby.

Keely takes Lucy's hand.

Keely	Put your hand here and you might feel it move.

She continues with the story:

. . . And this is the wood that Hansel and Gretel are lost in.

She draws some trees; she sees Student Nurse Gary Miller walking up the ward.

Keely Nurse Miller!!!

Nurse Miller That's me. Hiya Lucy, are you feeling better today then?

Lucy nods, but keeps her hand on Keely's lump.

Keely Her legs aren't stinging any more are they?

Lucy nods her head to mean 'Yes'.

Keely You fibber, you told me they weren't hurting.

Lucy smiles.

Keely speaks to Nurse Miller.

Keely She's late isn't she?

Nurse Miller She's got an assignment to do.

Keely What's it feel like to be showing another student nurse the ropes?

Nurse Miller It's like I'm getting somewhere at long last.

Keely When do you go to Women's Medical?

Nurse Miller End of the week, I'm not looking forward to it.

Keely They'll love you on there. Just think of it, all them women making a fuss of you.

He smiles at the thought.

Nurse Miller I suppose I could get to like it.

Keely We'll miss yer.

He looks proud.

Nurse Miller Yeah, yeah well the next time I'm back on this ward, I'm gonna be a fully qualified nurse.

Lucy smiles.

Lucy It moved.

We focus on Lucy's smiling face.

Danny Phillips, his leg in plaster, struggling to get off the trolley, is wheeled on to the children's ward. Katie Grahams (the new student nurse) accompanies him and has a firm hand on his shoulder. She wears puce-coloured tights, Doc Marten shoes and approximately six earrings in her right ear. Her hair is unkempt. An overbleached lock, which has a touch of pink to it, falls from under her hat. We see Nurse Mitchell's reaction. Auxillary Nurse Mags goes quickly over to Danny.

Danny Get off me. Stupid idiot! I don't wanna go in no bed!

Nurse Mags I take it you're Danny?

Danny I'm going home!!

Nurse Mags Not unless you can fly lovie.

Danny I am!!!

Nurse Mags I suppose you're the new recruit?

Nurse Grahams Katie Grahams. He tried to bite me hand.

Nurse Mags Nurse Miller!!! Get yourself over here.

Nurse Miller is already on his way down, feeling very superior in his new role as student supervisor.

Nurse Mags I believe you're looking after this young lady. Her name's Nurse Grahams.

He is slightly stunned by her appearance.

Nurse Miller Oh! Right, yes. Sorry. I didn't realise . . . I'm Nurse Miller. Hi!

Danny is struggling to get off the trolley.

Danny I'm not stopping here.

Nurse Grahams restrains him.

Nurse Grahams This is Daniel Philips, better known as Danny, but more accurately known as a complete pain in the backside.

Nurse Mags Will you keep still or else you'll be off there and then your other leg'll need plastering.

Nurse Grahams That'll be fun. . .

Danny I hate her!!!

Nurse Grahams I don't much like you either.

Danny	I want to get out of here. I want to go home!!!
Nurse Miller	I heard you the first time, there's no need to shout.
Danny	Shut your face.
Nurse Mags	Eh! That's enough of that.

Nurse Miller asserts his new status.

Nurse Miller	It's all right, Nurse Mags. He's got to stay until that plaster's set so you might as well get used to the idea.
Nurse Mags	He'll be a while after that an'all because it's his knee cap.

They are at the bed now. Nurse Mitchell enters the ward.

Danny	I want to go home!!!

Nurse Mitchell approaches.

Nurse Mitchell	My goodness, what's all the row about. I thought it was a baby screaming not a big grown boy.
Danny	Get lost!!!
Nurse Mags	It's all right, we're managing.
Nurse Mitchell	Now come on, there's a little girl over there with both legs scalded and she's not screaming and shouting.
Danny	I don't care. I want to go home . . . now!!!
Nurse Mags	We heard you the first time son and there's a simple answer to that: you can't. Right, let's get him on that bed; I think it's going to take all three of us.

Nurse Mitchell makes her way to the office.

Nurse Mitchell	I think we'll let Sister deal with this.
Nurse Mags	Oh! Come on, let's get it done.

Nurse Miller is assertive:

Nurse Miller	Right, Now there's two ways of doing this, there's the easy way or the hard way, and it's up to you, Danny.
Nurse Mags	Either way he's going on that bed.

Nurse Miller	Yes.
Danny	I'm not!!!
Nurse Mags	Oh yes you are, sunshine. You get the top end, Nurse Miller, I'll get his legs.
	Nurse Grahams stands by as Nurse Mags gets hold of his legs. Danny kicks out. Nurse Miller struggles to get hold of Danny's arms, and manages to restrain him.
Nurse Mags	One, two, three.
	They lift a writhing and shouting Danny on to the bed.
Danny	No!!! . . . I don't wanna go on no bed. . .
	Danny manages to free his arm from Nurse Miller's grip and lands out, hitting Nurse Miller straight across the face with his hand. Nurse Miller instinctively gives Danny a blow back, across his head.
Nurse Mags	Nurse Miller!!!
	Both Nurse Miller and Danny are totally stunned. The ward goes quiet. We see Nurse Mitchell standing with Sister Diane Meadows. They have just entered the ward. They move over to Nurse Miller.
	Nurse Miller is stunned.
Nurse Miller	I'm sorry, I didn't mean to. . .
	He can't think of what to say.
	Nurse Mags turns to Sister Meadows.
Nurse Mags	It was an accident.
Sister Meadows	I saw what happened, Nurse Mags.
Nurse Miller	I didn't mean to do it, but I did.
Sister Meadows	What's that supposed to mean? I can't say to the nursing officer, 'Oh he didn't mean to do it, but he did.'
Nurse Miller	I don't know what else to say.
Sister Meadows	I can't believe you sometimes. Fancy doing this

	to me.
Nurse Miller	I'm sorry.
Sister Meadows	That's no good is it?
Nurse Miller	I don't mean for hitting him, although I am sorry, but I wasn't saying it for that. I meant for putting you in this position.
Sister Meadows	Will you shut up, Nurse Miller, and let me think.

Nurse Mags has moved away is plumping some pillows up on an empty bed when Nurse Mitchell comes over to her.

Nurse Mitchell	Well that's the end of his career.
Nurse Mags	That make you happy does it?

Nurse Mitchell looks hurt.

Nurse Mitchell	No, it doesn't. What kind of person do you think I am?

Nurse Mags walks away, passing Keely. She is talking to Nurse Grahams and packing away some crayons which are on Lucy's bed. Nurse Grahams sits on the end of the bed. Nurse Mitchell approaches in the background . . . Keely is gobsmacked.

Keely	Fancy Nurse Miller smacking him one.
Nurse Grahams	He deserved it, I'd been dying to crack him one myself.
Nurse Mitchell	Hello, I'm Nurse Mitchell.
Nurse Grahams	Pleased to meet you. I'm Katie Grahams, new student.
Nurse Mitchell	Well, Nurse Grahams, we don't like staff sitting on beds in this ward. . .

Nurse Grahams stands quickly

Nurse Mitchell	. . . things are quite casual enough, but if you feel you have the time to sit, then find yourself a chair, all right?
Nurse Grahams	Fine.
Nurse Mitchell	Angela Jameson, at the end, needs a bed pan.

Nurse Mitchell marches off.

Keely Once you've learnt how to handle Dragon Breath, you've cracked it. Has anybody said anything about your tights?

Nurse Mags approaches.

Nurse Grahams What about my tights?

Keely Nothing.

Nurse Mags I hope Nurse Miller's gonna be all right. It isn't normally like this, love.

Nurse Grahams I thought it was quite exciting.

Nurse Mags starts to go off Nurse Grahams.

Nurse Mags Well, It's not very exciting for poor Nurse Miller, bless him. He'll be a nervous wreck. I just hope they ask me to make a report, because if they do I will tell 'em exactly what I think.

Nurse Grahams So will I.

Nurse Mags is not too sure about this girl.

Nurse Mags What will you say then?

Nurse Grahams I'll say that the patient is a bit loopy and should be on a psychiatric ward and that what's his name. . .

Nurse Mags and Keely Nurse Miller!!!

Nurse Grahams That's right . . . Nurse Miller, is geared up to working on a children's ward and not prepared for the torrent of abuse and violent behaviour displayed by the patient which consequently resulted in a spontaneous reflex action – I'd better go get that bed pan.

Nurse Mags and Keely are both gobsmacked.

Nurse Mags Yes, well that's what I shall say as well.

Nurse Grahams I should think he'll get the sack though. Smacking a patient is definitely not on.

She goes to get the bed pan.

Scene 9 *(Internal): Casualty waiting area*

Cal Spicer being pushed out of a treatment room in a wheelchair.

Cal   I was in the toilet combing me hair one minute, and the next I was in an ambulance. I can't remember what happened in between.

Scene 10 *(Internal): Darren's bed*

Darren is sitting playing a space invader game with James.

James   Come on, that's not fair.

Darren   I haven't finished.

James   You have.

Darren   I've got a free go.

James   They're all free you div.

Darren   If you shurrup I'll finish quicker.

James sees Cal entering the ward.

James   Hey! It's him.

Darren looks up.

Darren   Who?

James snatches the game.

James   Him wi' head on.

Darren   Hey, give it us back, Jim, I haven't finished. That's not fair.

But James is away down the ward with his space invader game. Darren speaks to Bryony.

Darren   Did you just see what he did?

Bryony   He's clever isn't he?

Darren   I'm gonna do him.

James passes Cal and Nurse Mitchell.

James   What are you doin' here?

Cal keeps moving.

Cal   Learning how to ice skate.

Cal goes to his bed, passing Darren. Darren catches up with James. He is aggressive.

Darren   Hey, it said 'go again'.

James   Yeah well it's my game, and I never said you could. Hey, you see him, last time I were in, he used to visit this lad that got stabbed. He's dead hard, he's my friend.

Darren   It's a stupid game anyway.

Bryony is watching Cal who is at the next bed to hers, unpacking his things into his locker.

Nurse Mitchell   Now is there anything you need?

Cal   Pint lager?

Nurse Mitchell   Very funny.

And she goes away.

Cal   I thought it was.

Bryony   You have to watch the nurses, they get tough sometimes.

Cal   How do you mean, tough?

Bryony is enjoying herself.

Bryony   You see him over there. Well, one of the nurses took a swing at him earlier on.

Cal   You're joking.

Bryony   I'm not.

Cal   Well if anyone touches me, I'll sue 'em . . . How long have you been in here?

Bryony   Three weeks.

Cal   Three weeks! What's up wi yer?

Bryony   Rheumatoid arthritis.

Cal   I thought only old biddies got that.

Bryony   No, you can get it at any age. I started with it years ago.

Cal   Have you come in here to get rid of it then?

Bryony   They can't get rid of it; they just make it a bit easier for me, that's all.

Cal	What you mean like never?
Bryony	I don't know, I just have to wait and see.
Cal	I wouldn't have that.
Bryony	I don't have much choice.

Cal contemplates this for a moment.

Bryony	What are you in for!
Cal	Nothing, there's nothing wrong with me.

Jack Crossley enters with his trolley.

Jack	Mind your backs. And I've no change for a start. Who wants what?

He asks Bryony first. He snaps at her.

Jack	Do you want anything then?
Bryony	Have you got any of them jelly coke bottles?

Jack is getting agitated.

Jack	I've got jelly spanners, penny chews and liquorice sticks.
Bryony	Aw!!!

Jack is now at exploding point.

Jack	I can't help it if the wholesalers haven't got 'em in.

Cal smirks. . .

Jack	What are you smirking about? I've seen you somewhere before. That's right, you were one of them hooligans that caused all that bother.
Cal	Go polish your head.
Jack	Cheeky brat! What you need is a good hiding! Bad through and through that one. Right I've no jelly coke bottles so what do you want?
Bryony	I'm all right thanks. I don't want anything.

Jack moves off.

Jack	You could have said that half an hour ago. I could have been on Maternity by now.

Scene 11 *(Internal): Ward office*

Sister Meadows is checking that her hat is on straight and her appearance is all right, before she goes up to see the nursing officer.

Sister Meadows When you saw what he was like, why didn't you come and get me?

Nurse Miller I thought we could manage.

Sister Meadows You didn't think you'd show this trendy new nurse how clever you are, did you?

Nurse Miller No, I didn't think that . . . I feel so stupid . . . She must think I'm a complete idiot.

Sister Meadows Well she wouldn't be far wrong would she?. . . I'm sorry, I just can't believe that you of all people could hit a patient.

Nurse Miller I've never hit anyone before.

The door opens. It is Dr Gallagher.

Dr Gallagher Dr Woods has been invited in on one of Anderton's operations. I've been trying to get in there for nearly two years.

Dr Gallagher goes over to the coffee machine.

Dr Gallagher So what's Nurse Grahams like, eh, Nurse Miller? Sorry, d'you want a coffee?

Sister Meadows Dr Gallagher.

Dr Gallagher Yes.

He realises the atmosphere in the room.

Dr Gallagher What's up?

Sister Meadows I'm working.

Dr Gallagher Oh I'm sorry, I didn't realise.

There is a knock on the door and Nurse Mags enters.

Nurse Mags Er, can I have a word?

Sister Meadows Can't it wait?

Nurse Mags Five minutes, that's all.

Sister Meadows gets up and leaves the room.

There is an awkward hiatus in the room between Nurse Miller and Dr Gallagher.

Dr Gallagher   Why don't you sit down.

Nurse Miller   I've lost me contact lens.

Dr Gallagher   You don't have to see to sit. Well smile, that's not the end of the world.

Scene 12 *(Internal): Waiting area outside ward office*

Nurse Mags   We're talking about our Nurse Miller – he wouldn't hurt a fly, Sister Meadows, and you know it.

Sister Meadows   Well he has hurt a fly, Nurse Mags. He hit a lad who was still traumatised from breaking his knee cap, a lad who is more than likely in a great deal of pain. If it had been anybody else you'd scream 'get 'em out'. Don't talk to me about 'our Nurse Miller.'

James comes tearing round the corner.

James   Nurse!!! That new boy's on the floor now.

Sister Meadows, Nurse Mags and James turn on to the ward. We see what they see – Danny on the floor, trying to pull himself up by the bed next to his. A few kids including James, Darren and Lucy watch on.

Nurse Mitchell   Get his legs, Nurse Grahams.

Nurses Mitchell and Grahams go to get hold of Danny's limbs. Sister Meadows approaches fast.

Sister Meadows   Just leave him there for the minute please.

Nurse Mitchell steps back. She is angry.

Nurse Mitchell   Anything you say, Sister.

Sister Meadows   Right young man, what do you think you're doing on the floor?

Danny   It beats hanging off the ceiling.

Sister Meadows	Oh, we've got a comedian have we? Well we could pull chairs round, sell tickets.
Danny	Can't keep me in here.
Sister Meadows	Not a moment longer than we have to. Nurse Mags, will you help me to lift the patient back on to his bed please?
	Nurse Mags is chuffed.
Nurse Mags	Certainly.
	They go to get an arm each but Danny holds his arms in tight to his body.
Danny	I'll just get back off again.
Sister Meadows	And we'll just put you back on again.
Nurse Grahams	What about putting the mattress on the floor and then he can't fall off.
Sister Meadows	Sounds like a good idea to me. I think you're going to go far, young lady.
	Nurse Mags catches sight of the fracture in Danny's plaster.
Nurse Mags	His pot's cracked.
	Sister Meadows gets angry.
Sister Meadows	Aw! That's great! He's gonna have to go back to replastering now.
Danny	I'm not going back down there again.
	Sister Meadows speaks to Nurse Mitchell.
Sister Meadows	Get it X-rayed and a bucket sent up.
	Nurse Mitchell follows Sister Meadows away.
Nurse Mitchell	I don't think we should give in to him, Sister. I think we should lift him straight back on. . .
Sister Meadows	My decision is made, Nurse Mitchell.
	She walks away. She has had enough! Nurse Mitchell is furious and mutters to herself.
Nurse Mitchell	Pardon me for thinking.

Scene 13 *(Internal): Operating theatre*

*Calm relaxing music is playing as Lee Jones'
operation is in progress. Several people are in
attendance including Dr Woods.*

Mr Anderton   I'm afraid it'll have to come out.

Grave looks are exchanged among those present.

Mr Anderton   Clips please. . .

And in true hospital style, the surgeon's hand
should be held out and a very efficient nurse
will place the instrument precisely in his hand.

Mr Anderton   And scissors. . .

Scene 14 *(Internal): Theatre waiting area*

*Mrs Jones sits waiting. Ben walks round the
corner; he has his school bag.*

Mrs Jones   Ben!

Ben   Oh hiya! I've brought his clothes and bags. I
thought he might need 'em, you know, for
coming home in.

Ben sits down next to her.

Mrs Jones   He won't be coming home; he's having an
operation.

Ben   An operation? What for?

Mrs Jones   His kidney. They'll be keeping him in.

Ben   . . . If we win the next match, or even draw,
we're into the semi-finals.

Mrs Jones' brain is elsewhere but she is trying.

Mrs Jones   Yeah.

Ben   But we won't win if we haven't got Lee, he's our
best player. Oh, Sean Devlin's all right, but he's
nowhere near as good as Lee.

Dr Woods approaches Mrs Jones.

Dr Woods   Everything's gone smoothly. Lee's had his
kidney removed, and he's come through it really
well.

Scene 15 *(Internal): Ward office*

Sister Meadows enters. She is angry. Dr Gallagher and Nurse Miller are still in the office.

Sister Meadows I've had enough today. I was supposed to be seeing the nursing officer ten minutes ago. Nurse Miller, go to the canteen and get yourself a cup of tea.

Nurse Miller I've just had a coffee.

This exasperates sister Meadows.

Sister Meadows Well go for a walk, go anywhere.

Nurse Miller I'll be in Ophthalmics.

Sister Meadows Right.

Nurse Miller leaves.

Dr Gallagher He's lost a contact lens.

Sister Meadows I suppose he's told you what happened?

Dr Gallagher nods.

Sister Meadows He shouldn't be on this ward.

Dr Gallagher He won't be on any ward soon.

Sister Meadows I'm not talking about Nurse Miller. I'm talking about Danny. He's a psychiatric case.

Dr Gallagher Let's not start bunging labels on people, eh.

Sister Meadows snaps back.

Sister Meadows Well he is. He's rude, he's totally disruptive and I'm not having it.

Dr Gallagher Don't get angry with me. It's not my fault.

Sister Meadows Yeah, well I've had a rotten day.

Scene 16 *(Internal): Children's ward*

Porters wheel Danny's bed away. A portable X-ray machine stands by. Danny's mattress is now on the floor. A polythene sheet is covering the mattress and Nurse Mitchell has a plastic tunic on. She is managing to repair Danny's plaster cast. Nurse Grahams holds the bucket of plaster.

Keely and Lucy are checking around the floor looking for Nurse Miller's contact lens. Nurse Mags holds Danny's leg still. The operation is going quite smoothly and Nurse Mitchell is having some success. Danny is opening a packet of cheese and onion crisps.

Nurse Mitchell speaks to Danny.

Nurse Mitchell   Do you carry on like this at home?

Danny   Yeah.

Nurse Mitchell soaks some gauze bandage in the bucket.

Nurse Mitchell   Well I pity your poor parents.

Nurse Mitchell applies the soaking gauze to the top of Danny's leg.

Danny   Oooh, it's running all down me leg.

He sits bolt upright, knocking the bucket of plaster out of Nurse Grahams' hand, all over Nurse Mitchell and on to the floor. Nurse Mitchell is covered in white plaster.

Nurse Mitchell   Oh, you stupid boy!!! I'm completely covered.

Nurse Mags and Nurse Grahams have to stifle a laugh.

Scene 17 *(Internal): Children's ward*

Darren, James and Cal are all sitting on Cal's bed. Lucy is sitting on Bryony's bed (next bed up). She is in her nightie. We see the stakes at the end of Cal's bed: The space invader game, a digital watch and a calculator. A game of Trivial Pursuit is under way. We come up on James' studious face.

Darren   Come on, you've been half an hour.

James   I'm thinking.

Lucy   I know the answer.

Darren   Well don't tell him. It's for a cheese.

James   Read it again.

Darren	He doesn't know. You're not gonna win anyway 'coz you've only got two cheeses and Cal's only got one to get.

Cal picks up the dice.

Cal	And it's my turn.

James speaks to Cal.

James	What's the answer then?
Lucy	Upside down.
Darren	You divvy.

Cal throws the dice.

James	I bet you didn't know.
Darren	Everybody knows how Mr Topsey Turvey wears his hat.
Cal	Four and that's blue for a cheese.

Cal wins the game and leaves, taking the booty from James and Darren.

Darren	I'm pig sick. He's got me Pac-man now.
James	Well you shouldn't have bet it, if you didn't want to lose it.
Darren	He made out like he was useless at Triv. and you're thick, so I thought I was gonna be a watch and calculator better off.
James	Me calculator dun't work, that's how thick I am.

They both turn to look at Cal, who is trying to fathom out how to get the calculator going.

Scene 18 *(Internal): Danny's mattress (next day)*

Danny pushes the duvet cover down to reveal his angry-looking face at being woken up.

Nurse Mitchell stands in front of him with a tray of breakfast.

Nurse Mitchell	Cereal?
Danny	I want some orange juice.
Nurse Mitchell	That's no way to ask is it. What's the magic word?

Danny replies insolently.

Danny   Abracadabra.

He puts the duvet cover back over his head.

Scene 19 *(Internal): Main corridor*

Psychedelic patterned legs running along the corridor.

Nurse Miller   You'll get into trouble.

*The legs stop. We see the owner of the legs –
Nurse Grahams. She turns and looks back to see
Nurse Miller dressed quite trendily, with his
glasses on.*

Nurse Miller   You're not supposed to run . . . ever.

Nurse Grahams   I know, but I'm late.

Nurse Miller   Then you'll be in double trouble.

As they walk along the corridor. . .

Nurse Grahams   What happened about yesterday?

Nurse Miller   I don't know. The nursing officer wants to see
me today. That's why I've come in.

Nurse Grahams   Well good luck.

Nurse Miller   Thanks, but I think it's more a miracle that I need.

*Nurse Mags is about to enter the office when she
sees Nurse Grahams.*

Nurse Mags   Come on, they're waiting for you.

Nurse Grahams gives Nurse Miller her coat.

Nurse Grahams   Hang this up for me will you?

*Both Nurse Miller and Nurse Mags stare at Nurse
Grahams. She has shortened and tapered her
uniform into a mini skirt. Her nails have been
painted black. She tries to stick her hair up under
the cap as she strides along the corridor clad in her
multicoloured tights. Nurse Grahams approaches
Nurse Mags.*

Nurse Mags   What have you got on?

Nurse Grahams	Clothes.

Nurse Grahams enters the office. Nurse Mags stays for a moment to reassure Nurse Miller.

Nurse Mags	You're gonna be fine, you tell her.

Nurse Mags goes into the office.

Scene 20 *(Internal): Renal intensive care*

Lee is lying in bed asleep. He still looks pale. Mrs Jones is still sitting by his side. Male nurse John Langdon wheels in the dialysis machine.

Nurse Langdon	Did you manage to get some sleep?
Mrs Jones	A couple of hours.

Lee opens his eyes; looks at the machine – it can look quite frightening at first. Lee speaks faintly – he is still sleepy.

Lee	What's that?
Nurse Langdon	A dialysis machine.

Lee closes his eyes again.

Nurse Langdon	He'll be all right.
Mrs Jones	Do you think so?
Nurse Langdon	Yeah, I know he looks a bit rough at the moment, but it's amazing how quickly they pick up.
Mrs Jones	I couldn't bear it if anything happened to him. He's all I've got.
Nurse Langdon	Nothing will.

He gives a reassuring smile.

Nurse Langdon	I won't let it.

We see the first glimmer of a smile on Mrs Jones' face.

Scene 21 *(Internal): Ward office*

The staff meeting is near the end now. Various members of the staff look at Nurse Grahams. Dr

Gallagher looks a touch fed up.

Sister Meadows OK, Nurse Mags what about you – do you think Danny should stay on this ward?

Nurse Mags Well he seems a bit quieter today.

Sister Meadows All right, for now he stays. Thank you all very much. The meeting's over.

Everybody gets up.

Once everyone apart from Sister Meadows has left, Nurse Miller knocks at the door and enters.

Nurse Miller I just thought I'd come to say goodbye.

Sister Meadows I'm sorry, I really am. What are you gonna do now?

Nurse Miller I don't know. Will it be OK if I come in from time to time, you know, to say hello to everyone?

Sister Meadows If you don't you'll be in trouble.

Nurse Miller Thanks for everything, I've loved working here . . . I'd better go. Will you tell everyone I said goodbye. I just don't feel like. . .

Sister Meadows Course I will.

She looks at him and goes to hug him.

Sister Meadows Aw! Nurse Miller, why did it have to be you.

Nurse Miller is choked, nearly moved to tears. He swallows hard.

Sister Meadows You'll find something else.

Nurse Miller only just manages to speak.

Nurse Miller Yeah. Bye then.

He goes to open the door, but it is stuck.

Nurse Miller I think it's er . . . stuck.

He struggles. Sister Meadows opens it for him.

Sister Meadows It doesn't want you to go.

He walks away.

Scene 22 *(Internal): Sparkies main staircase/foyer*

Nurse Grahams, having collected her coat from the locker room, is now marching off down the stairs, heading for the exit. She has her coat on and her nurses' hat off. Nurse Miller sees her.

Nurse Miller   Nurse Grahams! Where are you going?

He catches up with her. They walk together.

Nurse Grahams   Sister Meadows has sent me home. I'm not suitably dressed.

Nurse Miller   Yeah, they're funny about things like that.

Nurse Grahams   Means I've got the day off now.

Nurse Miller   So have I. . .

There is a pause whilst they walk.

Nurse Grahams   You didn't find your contact lens then?

Nurse Miller   No.

Nurse Grahams   You look much better in glasses anyway, they suit you. I prefer men in glasses. They look dead intelligent.

Nurse Miller lightens up a bit at this.

Nurse Miller   Really? . . . Look you don't wanna do something do you? . . . I mean what with you having the day off and like me getting the sack, I thought we could go somewhere.

Nurse Grahams   Why not.

Nurse Miller   Great. Where do you fancy going?

Nurse Miller smiles as they walk off together down the corridor – quite clearly the possible start of a romance.

Episode Two
by Kay Mellor

Scene 1 *(Internal): Children's ward*

Danny hurls a bowl of porridge across the room.

Danny I don't like it!!!

We see the various reactions to this, but particularly Nurse Mags who was the deliverer of the porridge. She glares at Danny whose mattress is still on the floor.

Nurse Mags Right! I've had about enough of you.

She marches off in the direction of the office. The ward is hushed and we see various responses from the other patients. Cal is amused.

Cal Guess he's not too keen on porridge.

Bryony ignores him and opens some birthday cards. Lucy is standing at the side of her bed watching her.

Lucy How old are you?

Bryony Fourteen. Do you want to help me open my cards?

Lucy shakes her head to mean 'no'. She sees a plate with toast crusts on.

Lucy Are you going to eat your crusts?

Bryony No, do you want them?

Lucy nods her head.

Bryony Go on then.

Lucy takes the toast crusts and runs back towards her bed.

Lucy goes over to Danny's bed. She takes her dummy out of her mouth to speak.

Lucy Why are you so horrible?

Danny Go play on the motorway.

Lucy	No, I'll get knocked down. Can I have your dinner if you don't want it?
	Danny shouts at her.
Danny	Scram!!!
	Lucy sticks her dummy back into her mouth. Nurse Mitchell is settling in a new admission: Philip Dean, who has come up from casualty with a burn to his hand and forearm.
Philip	Do I have to get in it?
Nurse Mitchell	Only if you want to go to sleep. Doctor will come and see you in a minute, all right?
Philip	Yeah.
	Nurse Mitchell goes. James looks at Philip.
James	What's wrong with you?
Philip	I've burnt me hand.
Darren	How did you do that?
Philip	I was trying to light a firework, only the stupid thing kept going out.
Darren	Is it all manky?
Philip	It's red. It didn't half hurt.
	Lucy approaches on her hunt for food.
Darren	I'm not allowed out on bonfire night because of my asthma.
James	I'm only allowed sparklers.
	Darren and Philip laugh. James picks on someone smaller than him.
James	You're too big to suck a dummy.
Darren	Leave her alone.
	Lucy recognises the tulle gras dressing on Philip's hand and arm. She takes her dummy out.
Lucy	You've got the same as me.
	She lifts her dress to show the dressing on her upper legs.
Philip	What have you done?

Lucy puts the dummy back in her mouth: She doesn't want to talk about it.

Darren She thought she'd play tea parties, only she used the real tea pot.

James We came in on the same day didn't we?

Lucy nods.

James And you've got six dummies in your drawer haven't you?

Lucy nods.

Philip What for?

Lucy takes the dummy out.

Lucy Spares.

Scene 2 *(Internal): Ward office*

Sister Meadows, Dr Gallagher and Dr Woods are all listening to Nurse Mags' tirade.

Nurse Mags I'm not having it.

Sister Meadows Calm down, Nurse Mags.

Nurse Mags He shouldn't even be on this ward. Nurse Miller got the sack because of him. What else has to happen before he goes?

Dr Woods We've got to get this sorted out.

Sister Meadows I think he should be in a psychiatric ward.

Dr Woods What do we know about him?

Nurse Mags He's crackers, that's what we know.

Dr Gallagher Have we seen his parents?

Sister Meadows They're visiting this afternoon.

Dr Woods And is he known to social services?

Sister Meadows Steve Bailey's coming in this morning.

Nurse Mags Someone better do something, or else I'll murder him.

Scene 3 *(Internal): Children's ward*

Nurse Grahams and Nurse Mags are cleaning up the porridge. Nurse Grahams has her hair done differently, beads etc hang from bits of it. She also wears a large leather non-uniformed belt, black thick woollen tights and Doc Martens. Her nails are free from nail varnish and she is without jewellery, except for the odd bead hung from her hair and the bits and bobs attached to the belt.

Nurse Mags	Anyway, where did you get to yesterday?
Nurse Grahams	I was sent home. Sister Meadows didn't like the way I was dressed.
Nurse Mags	And has she seen you today?
Nurse Grahams	No, I'm keeping out of her way. Me and Nurse Miller went to Blackpool.
Nurse Mags	You and Nurse Miller!?
Nurse Grahams	Yes, why what's the matter with him?
Nurse Mags	Nothing, he's lovely.
Nurse Grahams	He's all right. We're going out on Thursday as well.

Nurse Mitchell calls out from across the ward.

Nurse Mitchell	Nurse Mags!!!

Mags is annoyed as she wanted to hear all the news.

Nurse Mags	I'm coming.

We leave Nurse Grahams still wiping the floor down and go with Nurse Mags up to Lucy's bed.

Nurse Mitchell	What are you smiling about?

Nurse Mags is relishing the secret.

Nurse Mags	Oh! Nothing.
Nurse Mitchell	Can you start on Lucy's bed?
Nurse Mags	Where is she?
Nurse Mitchell	In the dayroom, I imagine.

Nurse Mags pulls back the duvet cover to find a tortoise sitting in the middle of the bed amidst some toast crusts. Nurse Mags screams.

Nurse Mags   Ahhhh!!!

Nurse Mitchell is alarmed.

Nurse Mitchell   What is it?

All eyes on Nurse Mags.

Nurse Mags   A tortoise, I think.

Darren, Phillip and James bomb over to Lucy's bed.

Darren   Where did that come from?

Nurse Mags   I've no idea. It was just there.

James   It's big in't it?

Nurse Mitchell   Where's Lucy?

She marches off.

Philip   What you gonna do with it?

Nurse Mags   Don't ask me, I don't like the things.

Nurse Mags, clearly cannot see the creature's appeal.

Scene 4 *(Internal): Children's ward*

Nurse Mitchell emerges from the dayroom. She is searching for Lucy.

Hospital DJ (voice only).

DJ   So tomorrow's the night for all the witches and spooks to fright. So all you trick or treaters, do your stuff. I wonder if Sparkies has a ghostie?

He makes a ghoul sound.

DJ   Let me know if you've seen anything. . .

Nurse Mitchell heads down the ward, and as she turns into the main corridor, she sees Lucy turning at the top of the stairs.

Nurse Mitchell   And where do you think you've been?

Lucy gets her dummy out of her dressing-gown pocket and sticks it in her mouth.

Nurse Mitchell What have you got there?

Lucy opens her hand to show a cabbage leaf.

Nurse Mitchell And I wonder who that's for?

Scene 5 *(Internal): Renal intensive care*

Mrs Carol Jones is sitting with Lee. Nurse Langdon is washing Lee down. Mrs Jones notices the dressing on Lee's arm.

Mrs Jones What's the matter with his arm?

Nurse Langdon Lee's had a fistula made.

Lee What's that?

Nurse Langdon An artery and a vein are joined together to make the blood flow at a much higher pressure and the vein will get bigger.

Ben Rowlingson knocks on the door, enters and sits at the side of Lee's bed.

Ben So, how y'doin'?

Lee I'm all right.

Mrs Jones I'll go get some breakfast, love, I'll be back soon.

Lee OK.

Mrs Jones goes.

Lee So who won?

Ben Nobody. The game was cancelled.

Lee But we had Sean Devlin in reserve.

Ben Yeah, but the ref wasn't there; Mr Appleyard went with you.

Lee Did he? I don't remember.

Dr Woods and Dr Gallagher enter.

Dr Woods Good morning Lee.

Lee Morning.

Dr Woods This is Dr Gallagher.

Lee	Hello.
Dr Gallagher	Hi.
Dr Woods	And are you Lee's brother?
Lee	I don't have a brother.
Ben	I'm just a friend.
Dr Gallagher	How are you feeling today?
Lee	All right.
Dr Woods	And today's your big day isn't it?
	Dr Woods is referring to the dialysis machine.
Lee	That thing.
Dr Woods	You're not worried are you?
Lee	I don't know why I have to have it, I feel all right.
Dr Woods	Hasn't anybody explained it to you?
Lee	I know why I've got this on my arm; so I can plug into that. It's something to do with my blood.
Dr Woods	That's right, but until the fistula's ready we'll be using a subclavian line. Your kidneys filter your blood and send all the rubbish and toxic wastes down to your bladder.
Dr Gallagher	But in your case, you haven't got that filter bed, so the poisons will build up in your body.
Dr Woods	So we have to find another method and this is it.
Dr Gallagher	It sucks your blood out, gives it a wash, and pumps it all back in again. Clean as a whistle.
Lee	So when are they coming to plug me in?
Dr Woods	I don't know. I'll find out. Mr Anderton will come and have a word with you first. Are you sure you're all right?
	Lee nods.
Dr Woods	There's a posh word for this you know – you can show off to your mates. It's called haemodialysis.
Dr Gallagher	I bet you always wanted to know that didn't you?
	Lee smiles.
Dr Woods	I'll be back later.

Dr Gallagher	See yer.
	They head off towards the door.
Lee	So when are we playing them?
Ben	In three weeks' time, but we've got Donisthorpe before then.
Lee	It'll be OK. Once I've had this done I'll be sound.
	Dr Woods glances at Dr Gallagher. She heard that little exchange.

Scene 6 *(Internal): Dayroom*

Witches' hats are on several children's heads. Some wear them and some paint them. Other children are busy scooping out swede ready for Hallowe'en lanterns. The door opens. It is Nurse Mitchell with Lucy. Lucy is clutching her tortoise. She is upset and sucking her dummy.

Nurse Mitchell	Do you have a box or anything suitable for a tortoise to live in for a little while?
	The children go over to look at Lucy with the tortoise.
Keely	Who's is that?
Lucy	Mine. He was crying for me.
Nurse Mitchell	Well it certainly can't stay on the ward.
Keely	Where's it come from?
Lucy	My house. I brought him in my bag.
Nurse Mitchell	He's been here since the day you came in?
	Lucy nods.
Nurse Mitchell	In your bed?
	Lucy nods.
Nurse Mitchell	Well that says something about the standard of this ward.
Keely	What about the sandpit?
Lucy	He likes sand.
Keely	Do they eat swede?

Lucy	It's his favourite.

Scene 7 *(Internal): Ward office*

Danny's parents Mr and Mrs Phillips are sitting down. Sister Meadows is behind the desk and Steve to one side of the desk.

Mrs Phillips	We've tried everything with him haven't we, Peter?
Mr Phillips	Everything.
Mrs Phillips	He's just highly spirited.
Mr Phillips	That's right.
Mrs Phillips	Some boys are like that.
Sister Meadows	You don't think it could be just plain bad behaviour.
Steve Bailey	Has he been in trouble before?
Mrs Phillips	No, not really.
Sister Meadows	According to his medical file, he's had several doctors.
Mrs Phillips	We've moved a lot, haven't we, Peter?
Mr Phillips	That's right.
Sister Meadows	Do you ever tell him off?
Mrs Phillips	Yes, his dad's always shouting at him, aren't you, Peter?
Mr Phillips	That's right, I'm always shouting at him.

Dr Woods and Dr Gallagher enter.

Steve Bailey	Has he ever been seen by a child psychiatrist?
Mrs Phillips	I don't think so. Do you know, Peter?
Mr Phillips	I don't think so.
Steve Bailey	How many schools has he been to?
Mrs Phillips	You're asking a lot of questions.
Sister Meadows	Because we need some answers.
Mrs Phillips	Well I'm not sure . . . about ten.
Mr Phillips	Ten, that's right.

Sister Meadows is exasperated at this.

Sister Meadows Why has he been to ten schools, Mrs Phillips?

Mrs Phillips 'Coz we've moved a lot.

Dr Woods Why?

Mrs Phillips speaks to her husband.

Mrs Phillips Why did we move?

Mr Phillips Don't ask me, it was you that wanted to move.

Mrs Phillips I think it was because we wanted to try a better school. Yes, that's it.

Dr Woods replies pointedly.

Dr Woods Or perhaps just another school.

Mrs Phillips A change is as good as a rest.

Dr Gallagher is losing patience.

Dr Gallagher How long has Danny behaved like this?

Mrs Phillips He can be really good sometimes, can't he?

Mr Phillips Sometimes . . . but mainly he's bad.

Mrs Phillips looks at Mr Phillips as though he has betrayed her.

Mr Phillips She can't stand it when he starts you see, so he gets his own way.

Mrs Phillips I'm bad with me nerves.

Mr Phillips I used to have a go at him, but she used to get so upset. We should never have had him.

Scene 8 *(Internal): Children's ward*

Cal is sitting in bed having a game of Trivial Pursuit with Nurse Grahams.

Cal One, two, three, four . . . and throw again. . .

He throws the dice again.

Cal . . . two. . .

Paces out the number.

Cal . . . one, two, pink for a cheese.

	Nurse Grahams takes a card out of a box. Nurse Grahams reads. Cal holds on to the dice.
Nurse Grahams	Which frog has a nephew called Robin?
	Cal throws the dice again.
Cal	Kermit. . .
	Reads the dice.
Cal	. . . four . . . throw again.
	He moves his dice to a grey square.
Nurse Mags	Are you some sort of Trivial Pursuit whizz-kid?
Cal	No, just lucky.
	And the game continues as. . .
DJ	(*voice only*) That was good old Kylie for Joanna Riley. And I've got a card here telling me that it's Bryony Shaeffer's birthday today. She's fourteen years old, so have a lovely day, Bryony, and hurry up and get better, from everybody on the children's ward.
	The DJ plays 'Life's what you make it.'
Nurse Grahams	Are you a fan of this music?
	Bryony beams.
Bryony	Yeah.
Cal	I'm in the middle. Right you can ask me any question you want now. Just choose one.
	Nurse Grahams speaks to Bryony.
Nurse Grahams	What colour shall I go for?
	Bryony is listening to her record.
Bryony	He's good at them all.
Nurse Grahams	Right then, for the game, green. . .
	She chooses a card and reads.
Nurse Grahams	What does a camel's hump mostly consist of?
	Cal pretends that he's thinking about it.
Cal	. . . er . . . I think it's . . . fat. Am I right?
	Nurse Grahams teases him.

Nurse Grahams	No you're wrong!
	She tells the truth.
Nurse Grahams	You've won.
Bryony	Told you.
	James appears back from the hospital radio.
James	Can I have another game?
	Cal packs the box up.
Cal	Later on.

Scene 9 *(Internal): Children's ward*

Danny is lying on his mattress. He looks quite calm and serene. Nurse Mitchell passes him. A record is playing on the hospital radio.

Nurse Mitchell	Are you all right?
Danny	I can't see anything down here.
Nurse Mitchell	What a shame.
	Steve Bailey the social worker arrives and sits on the mattress; Mr and Mrs Phillips join him and sit on chairs.
Steve Bailey	So what's all this about?
Danny	All what?
Steve Bailey	Come on, you know what.
Mrs Phillips	You've been playing up again haven't you?
Danny	Go home!
Steve Bailey	Don't you like it here?
Danny	No.
Mr Phillips	He doesn't like it anywhere.
Steve Bailey	Is that right?
	Danny is becoming increasingly restless.
Danny	Go away. I want the Nurse. Nurse!!!
	Nurse Grahams comes over.
Nurse Grahams	Yes?

Danny is now over-anxious.

Danny I want them all to go. I don't want them here. Tell them to go away.

Steve Bailey It's all right, we're going.

Mrs Phillips I only came to see how you were.

Mr Phillips He doesn't want us here.

Scene 10 *(Internal): Ward office*

Sister Meadows sits working as Dr Gallagher and Dr Woods talk.

Dr Gallagher Have you spoken with his mother?

Dr Woods Yes, I think she understands, but I don't think Lee's taken it in at all.

Dr Gallagher I'm sure Mr Anderton will explain it all to him.

Dr Woods Yeah, but you can listen to someone without hearing what they're saying.

I mean there he was going on about playing football again.

Steve enters.

Steve Bailey Well he's a tough nut to crack.

Sister Meadows Danny?

Steve Bailey Yeah and his parents . . . well what do you do?

Dr Gallagher I felt a bit sorry for them. They're well out of their depth.

Sister Meadows I think he's been allowed to get away with it for years and now it's a problem.

Dr Woods Have we checked all the obvious things, like a possible tumour or old head injury?

Steve Bailey We should check everything, but I really think it's more a behaviour problem than anything medical.

Sister Meadows Could he have some sort of mental illness?

Dr Woods It's a possibility.

Dr Gallagher We could get Dr Khan to take a look at him.

Sister Meadows	Well I just hope you're going to supervise him, because I can't afford to lose any more staff.

Scene 11 *(Internal): Renal intensive care*

Lee is in the process of having dialysis. We see the machine working.

Lee	It feels weird.
Nurse Langdon	Does it hurt?
Lee	No.
Nurse Langdon	Good.

Nurse Langdon checks everything is OK and working well.

Nurse Langdon	Where's your mother today?
Lee	She's gone to get me some clean pyjamas.
Nurse Langdon	I heard you had a visitor earlier?
Lee	Me mate from school. He had this morning off.
Nurse Langdon	So there's just you and your mum at home then?
Lee	Yeah.

Scene 12 *(Internal): Car*

Lee's brother Marcus, aged seventeen, is at the wheel. His father Eddie Jones sits in the passenger seat. Marcus turns the engine off.

Mr Jones	Right then, are you coming up to see him or what?

Marcus answers firmly.

Marcus	I'll wait here.
Mr Jones	Sure?
Marcus	Yep.
Mr Jones	He is your brother, Marcus.

Marcus is still resolute.

Marcus	I said . . . I'll wait here.

He puts a tape cassette on. Mr Jones decides not to push it and gets out of the car and walks away.

Scene 13 *(Internal): Corridor leading to renal intensive care*

Dr Woods Mrs Jones! . . . May I have a word?

Mrs Jones I just had to go pay a few bills and get some things for Lee.

Dr Woods It's not a problem . . . He's had his first dialysis this morning.

Mrs Jones sounds anxious.

Mrs Jones Yes, they said they were . . . I wanted to be there but. . .

Dr Woods It's nothing to be frightened of.

Mrs Jones I'm not . . . It's just I had to. . .

She knows it is just an excuse, and lets it go.

Mrs Jones Is he all right?

Dr Woods He's fine, no problems at all.

Mrs Jones I can only cope with one thing at a time. It's all been such a shock.

Dr Woods I understand. You'll get used to seeing him on dialysis and you'll get so that you can help him.

Mrs Jones I hope so.

Dr Woods He really does need you . . . I don't think he realises what he's had done. He was talking about playing football this morning.

Mrs Jones Oh! He lives for his football. That's what he wants to do when he leaves school. He's had a few trials and they're watching him.

Dr Woods He's going to have to rethink that . . . He's going to need dialysis two or three times a week. He's on a restricted diet and he has a fistula which needs protecting. I'm sorry, but he's not going to be able to play a hard game of football ever again.

Scene 14 *(Internal): Renal intensive care*

Lee has just completed his dialysis. Nurse Langdon is re-dressing the subclavian. An animated discussion about football is underway.

Lee There's only one team worth supporting, Man. United.

Nurse Langdon Come on . . . Liverpool's the best.

Lee scoffs and pretends to be gobsmacked.

Lee Liverpool!

Nurse Langdon What's wrong with Liverpool?

Lee What's right with 'em?

Nurse Langdon Well for a start they've the best player in the country.

Lee Who's that?

Nurse Langdon John Barnes.

Mrs Jones enters. Lee is totally engrossed in the conversation.

Lee John Barnes!!! Oh, come on. Everybody know's Brian Robson's the best, he wasn't England's captain for nothing.

Nurse Langdon Hiya.

Mrs Jones notices that Lee is well enough to argue!

Mrs Jones He's all right then?

Nurse Langdon Fighting fit.

Lee You missed the star attraction, Mam.

Mrs Jones I'll catch it next time.

Lee is fed up at this.

Lee Do I have to have it done again?

Nurse Langdon You certainly do, not for a couple of days though.

Lee changes the subject.

Lee We'll see who's got the best player anyway, 'coz we've got you in the League in a couple of weeks.

Nurse Langdon You'll be disappointed.

Lee Rubbish! I agree he's good, he can kick the ball around the field, but he's got no bottle.

Mrs Jones' eyes are beginning to fill up with tears

as she watches her young son discussing football with such enthusiasm.

Lee No . . . no you've got it all wrong, you've got it just go for it.

Nurse Langdon He's the most skilled footballer we've got and football is all about skill.

Lee Yeah, we know that, but sometimes you've got to boot it in. He thinks about it too much. You've got to go for it; you've got to want it that much nothing'll stop you. All you see is the back of that net, and all you hear is your own mind telling you to do it and nothing else matters.

Nurse Langdon And you don't think John Barnes has got that?

Lee answers with sheer determination.

Lee No, but I have.

Mrs Jones leaves the room.

Scene 15 *(Internal): Corridor outside renal intensive care*

As Mrs Jones leaves the renal unit, tears spill down her face. She tries to wipe them away, but as fast as she does, more appear – the tension of the last few days and hearing Lee talk about football catches up on her. Further down the corridor Mr Jones is walking purposefully towards the renal unit. Mrs Jones is trying desperately to control her emotions. She looks up, almost instinctively sensing her estranged husband is near. Her face freezes as her eyes fall upon him.

Mrs Jones What do you want?

Mr Jones I've come to see my son.

Mrs Jones He doesn't want to see you.

Mr Jones You've been crying.

Mrs Jones So. It's none of your business.

Mr Jones Is he in there?

Mrs Jones	You've never bothered with him before, so what you bothering with him now for?
Mr Jones	You know why I haven't seen him.
Mrs Jones	'Coz he doesn't want to see you that's why.
Mr Jones	Because you've poisoned his mind against me, that's why.
Mrs Jones	Like you've poisoned our Marcus's.
Mr Jones	Marcus is old enough to make up his own mind.
Mrs Jones	With a bit of help from you, you mean.
Mr Jones	There's nothing stopping you seeing Marcus. I won't stand in your way.
Mrs Jones	Oh! Yeah and I'm just likely to come round with her there.
Mr Jones	She's never done anything wrong to you.
Mrs Jones	If he wants me, he knows where he can find me.
Mr Jones	What's wrong with him?
Mrs Jones	Who told you he was in hospital?
Mr Jones	I have friends.

Mrs Jones answers sarcastically.

Mrs Jones	Oh! I forgot about you and your friends.
Mr Jones	Yeah, friends that tell me when my wife's making a fool out of me.
Mrs Jones	The only person that made a fool out of you was yourself. He was a friend that's all. . .

Nurse Langdon comes out of the renal unit.

Nurse Langdon	Everything all right?
Mrs Jones	Fine.
Mr Jones	Is Lee in there?
Nurse Langdon	Yes, do you want to see him? You can go in if you like.
Mrs Jones	I'll tell him you're here.

She goes in leaving Mr Jones standing outside with Nurse Langdon.

Nurse Langdon	He's a good kid.

Scene 16 *(Internal): Renal intensive care*

Lee's face is set. He still looks pale, but more animated from his discussion with Nurse Langdon.

Lee No way.

Mrs Jones He's outside.

Lee I don't want to see him. Get rid of him.

The door opens and Mr Jones enters.

Mr Jones Lee.

Mrs Jones He doesn't want to see you.

Mr Jones How you doing?

Lee Tell him to go, Mam.

Mrs Jones You heard him.

Mr Jones Lee, what happened with your mam and me has nothing to do with you. I still love you. You're still my son.

Lee Will you bring me telly in, Mam, there's a match on tomorrow.

Mr Jones Did you hear me?

Mrs Jones He doesn't want you here.

Mr Jones This isn't right, Lee. I can't just let you go.

No response from Lee.

Mr Jones I'll come back another time.

Scene 17 *(Internal): Renal intensive care*

We see Mr Jones as he walks away from the renal unit and his son. His heart is heavy. He has been hurt. Mr Jones passes Danny being wheeled back from the scan room, escorted by Dr Gallagher and Nurse Grahams.

Danny So do I need a new brain then?

Dr Gallagher Nope! The one you've got's fine.

Nurse Grahams That's a matter of opinion.

Danny You think you're clever don't you?

Nurse Grahams	I wouldn't sling porridge round like some two-year-old having a temper tantrum if that's what you mean.

Scene 18 *(Internal): Children's ward*

We are at Bryony's bed. Nurse Mags is plumping Bryony's pillows up.

Nurse Mags	Are you all right, pet?
Bryony	Yes thanks.
Nurse Mags	You'll be going for your hydrotherapy tomorrow.
Bryony	It'll be great just to get out of this bed.
Nurse Mags	I know, it must be awful, but are you feeling any better?
Bryony	A bit.
Nurse Mags	Good . . . Oh! and by the way, many happy returns.

Bryony smiles.

Bryony	Thanks.

Nurse Mags turns to Cal

Nurse Mags	Now then young man, are you all right?

Cal is playing with James' Pac-man game.

Cal	Yeah!
Nurse Mags	James has got one just like that.

Nurse Mags walks down the ward towards Lucy's bed. We take a moment first on Cal, pleased with himself, then a moment on Bryony, observing Cal.

Lucy is on the floor at the side of the bed, pushing a box with her tortoise in well under.

Nurse Mags	What yer doing?

Lucy spins round. She looks guilty. Nurse Mags bobs down at the side of the bed, Lucy-level.

Nurse Mags	He's supposed to be in the dayroom.
Lucy	He was lonely.
Nurse Mags	You'll get me shot. All right, if you don't say

anything, neither will I. Now get into bed.

Lucy's eyes light up and she scampers into her bed.

Nurse Mags   Night night sweetheart.

We follow Nurse Mags down the ward towards Danny's bed.

Nurse Mags   You're back then? Do you need anything?

Danny   I want something to drink.

Nurse Mags   Please.

Danny   Please.

A surprised Nurse Mags goes off to get Danny something to drink. Cal is putting his Trivial Pursuit cards back in order. We see that Bryony is watching him. She realises that the cards are placed in a certain order. Cal turns to check Bryony is not watching him. Bryony quickly closes her eyes and pretends to be alseep. Cal carries on sorting out his cards. Nurse Mags has brought a full water-jug back. She puts it on Danny's locker.

Nurse Mags   There y'are.

Danny picks the water jug up and drops it.

Nurse Mags   I don't believe you.

Danny tells an obvious lie.

Danny   It slipped.

We see that Nurse Mags could easily hit Danny. Dr Gallagher has entered the ward and intervenes.

Dr Gallagher   Go home, Nurse Mags.

Nurse Mags swings round.

Nurse Mags   Did you see that?

Dr Gallagher   Your shift's finished, Nurse Mags.

Nurse Mags   Well who's going to wipe that lot up?

Dr Gallagher   Me.

Nurse Mags   He did it on purpose.

Danny   The handle was slippy.

Dr Gallagher goes over to Danny's locker.
Dr Gallagher speaks to Nurse Mags.

Dr Gallagher Go.

Nurse Mags is heard muttering as she goes.

Nurse Mags I've seen some things in my time, but that beats the lot of them.

Danny What are you doing?

Dr Gallagher wheels the locker away.

Dr Gallagher Two days of good behaviour and you get your locker back.

Danny You can't do that.

Dr Gallagher Watch me.

Scene 19 *(Internal): Central corridor/locker*

Nurse Mags heads down the corridor towards the locker room to get her coat. She enters the locker room only to find Nurse Miller there, stuffing all his belongings into a bag. Nurse Mags is startled to find anyone in the locker room.

Nurse Mags Oh God! You frightened me to death.

Nurse Miller Sorry, I thought . . . well I thought you might have all gone . . . home.

Nurse Mags What yer doing?

Nurse Miller Just clearing my locker out. I er . . . I didn't. . .

Nurse Mags You wanted to sneak in and out without anyone seeing yer.

Nurse Miller Yes.

Nurse Mags With not even a tara for your mate and mucker.

Nurse Miller Course I wanted to see you, I wanted to see everyone. I want it all to go away, but it won't . . . I feel like I've let you all down.

Nurse Mags You do talk rubbish sometimes.

Nurse Miller It's the truth. I just couldn't face any of you.

Nurse Mags is upset.

Nurse Mags	Hey! Gary Miller. You were a good nurse and don't you forget it.
Nurse Miller	I wasn't, Nurse Mags. If I'd have been a good nurse then I wouldn't have hit Danny.
Nurse Mags	Listen, I could knock his block off for two pins.
Nurse Miller	But you don't do you. That's what it comes down to at the end of the day: you don't.
Nurse Mags	I can't believe you're just gonna wipe out all that training.
Nurse Miller	I haven't got much choice.
Nurse Mags	Fight!
Nurse Miller	If I thought they were wrong I would, but they're not . . . I've got to find something else.
Nurse Miller	Aw! Love.
	She goes up to him and gives him a big hug.
Nurse Mags	We're gonna miss you.

Scene 20 *(Internal): Renal intensive care*

Lee is asleep. Nurse Langdon sits by his side. Mrs Jones enters. She looks worried.

Mrs Jones	I don't know how to tell him.
Nurse Langdon	Do you want me to?
Mrs Jones	No, I've got to do it.
	Lee opens his eyes.
Lee	Tell me what?
Nurse Langdon	Do you want me to go?
Mrs Jones	If you don't mind.
	He goes.
Lee	Am I gonna die or something?
	Mrs Jones sits down.
Mrs Jones	No, you're doing well. They're really pleased with you . . . but there are some things that you're not going to be able to do any more.

Lee	I know, I can't eat certain things and I have to go on this. . .
Mrs Jones	Play football . . . not like you wanted to anyway.
	There is a stunned silence.
Lee	Well I might as well be dead then.
	Mrs Jones is distraught.
Mrs Jones	Lee, there is more to life than just football.
Lee	It's what I want.
Mrs Jones	You'll find other things you can do well.
Lee	I don't want anything else . . . I'm going to be a footballer, Mam. I'm going to play for Manchester United.
	We see Lee's determined face.

Episode Three
by Paul Abbot

Scene 1 *(External): Sparkies grounds*

A piece of spare land close to the hospital has been ear-marked for the bonfire night. 'Round Table' members and friends of the hospital are already at work, cordoning off a 50-metre diameter space. Some of them are unloading wood from a newly arrived wagon.

DJ   *(voice only)* . . . It's nine-oh-one and we're having f-u-n! Sparkie Hospital Radio coming direct from somebody's cupboard! A request from the renal unit who're losing Lee Jones today. He's moving to Children's ward. B1. Least it's nearer the front door, Lee! And you're just in time – I believe they're in for a Guy Fawkes rave-up tonight. Rumour has it, I'm the only one not invited. Good morning Sparkies!

He cues in music.

Scene 2 *(Internal): Children's ward*

Bryony is coming back from toilets as Darren and James head for dayroom. She blocks their thoroughfare with her wheelchair.

Bryony   I've got one thing to say to you.

James   What?

Bryony   Sucker! You played Trivial Pursuit with Cal and bet your Walkman, didn't you?

Darren   I warned him about underestimating the enemy. 's not James' fault he's a bit slow at Triv.

Bryony   Mustn't be your's either, then? Soccer boots and a U2 T-shirt? I've been watching.

Darren is embarrassed.

James   You never said.

Darren   You never asked!

He speaks to Bryony.

Darren   I'd got him down for a real dumbo.

Bryony   And neither of you have sussed what he's
playing at. . .

*Cal passes them ostentatiously enjoying the
Walkman that strictly belongs to James. He smiles
as he goes.*

James   How d'you mean?

Bryony   They weren't fair games, you know. Cal's got as
much up there as a breeze block.

Bryony returns to her bed. Darren shouts after her.

Darren   So how come he always wins?

Bryony   He cheats!

*Bryony disappears. Darren and James pursue her.
Bryony sneaks Cal's Trivial Pursuit pack out of his
locker. She spreads out the first 20 or so cards for
Darren and James.*

Bryony   Recognise any of the questions?

Darren   Yeah, I got that one.

James   And I got that one. And that one.

Bryony   You all got the same questions. He's fixed them.
He knows all the answers because he memorises
them. He's about as honest as Fagin!

James   Rip off!

Darren   How do you know all this?

Bryony   I've been watching him. That's what bed rest
means. You're so bored you have to take an
interest in the people around you. Even if they
happen to be Cal.

Darren   I'll do him! I want me boots back. And me T-shirt.

Bryony smiles knowingly.

Bryony   You could – if you play your cards right.

She produces a second set of Trivial Pursuit from under her bedclothes.

Bryony   Your *own* cards, I mean.

Bryony   You'll have rehearsed all the answers, just like he does. Then all you have to do is take his pack. . .

(which James is holding)

Bryony   . . .change his sequence of cards and you've caught him, but you can't do that till the last minute. . .

Scene 3 *(Internal): Danny's bed*

Nurse Mags is finishing tidying Danny's sheets.

Nurse Mags   There you go, Danny. We're clear of court martials now.

She turns to go.

Danny mutters quietly.

Danny   Fatso.

Nurse Mags is stunned.

Nurse Mags   I beg your pardon?

Danny   What?

Nurse Mags   Did you just call me a name?

Danny knots his sheets with his hand.

Danny   I'm not talking to you.

Nurse Mags is not sure what to make of this – cannot decide whether she heard wrong. But she gives him the benefit of the doubt and continues walking away.

Scene 4 *(Internal): Children's ward*

Nurse Langdon arrives with Lee in a wheelchair, accompanied by Nurse Mitchell who carries Lee's file.

Nurse Langdon   Happy now?

Lee	Ish. I'd be a lot happier if they were sending me home. Better than the renal ward, though – they're all old blokes in there.
	Nurse Langdon speaks to Nurse Mitchell.
Nurse Langdon	That's the youngest intake we've had for years.
Nurse Mitchell	Say you're over 25 to this lot and they treat you like cabbages.
Nurse Mags	Hello, Lee. I'm Nurse Mags. It's me you should thank for the clean sheets, the fresh water and cheerful service . . . But I don't suppose you will.
Lee	Thanks, Nurse Mags.
Nurse Mitchell	As soon as Dr Woods has taken a look at you, you can start circulating. . .
	Nurse Mitchell exits.
Nurse Mags	I believe he. . .
	She points to Nurse Langdon.
Nurse Mags	. . .comes with you?
Lee	He's me minder, aren't you, Nurse Langdon?
Nurse Langdon	Minder, nursemaid, confidant, punch bag . . . Where would you be without me?
Lee	Home?
	Nurse Mags is amused. She speaks to Nurse Langdon.
Nurse Mags	I think you're on a hiding to nothing there.
	Nurse Mags exits.
Lee	Will I be coming back to the renal unit for dialysis?
Nurse Langdon	No, we've made arrangements with Dr Anderton – we'll do it here. A portable machine goes anywhere you can.
Lee	I'd like to put that one to the test. Maine Road on a Sat'day?
	Nurse Langdon changes his tone - he is serious now.
Nurse Langdon	Come on, Lee.

Lee	What?
Nurse Langdon	Just ease off the big football talk, you're worrying your mum.
Lee	*She's* worried?
Nurse Langdon	I know it's a bummer, but your body's trying to cope with a major trauma right now. The last thing it needs is threatening with heavy duty sport.
Lee	I can *talk* about it, can't I?
Nurse Langdon	Course. But try doing some thinking, too. This operation's going to change your life. I'll be happier when you start facing facts. Football's a no-go. Right?

Lee does not respond.

Scene 5 *(Internal): Treatment room*

Cal is walking a straight line towards Dr Kahn and Dr Gallagher.

Dr Kahn	Last one. Can you touch the tip of your nose with your index finger?
Cal	What is this, the Krypton Factor or what?
Dr Kahn	Cal, did you experience any sense of dizziness before you lost consciousness?

Cal is stubbornly uninformative.

Cal	Nope.
Dr Kahn	Any strange smells, tastes?
Cal	No.
Dr Kahn	Do you know how long you were out for?
Cal	No.

Dr Kahn looks at Dr Gallagher hopelessly. He is getting nowhere. Dr Gallagher takes Cal aside and speaks quietly to him.

Dr Gallagher	He's a busy man, don't give him a hard time.
Cal	I din't ask to come here. You said you'd keep me

    in for 48 hours' observation. I've done that now and you've found nothin'. Can't I just go home?

Pause.

Dr Kahn   There's a note in your file that questions solvent abuse.

Cal   Sniffing glue?

Dr Kahn   That's one option.

Cal   Who put that in there?

He looks accusingly at Dr Gallagher.

Cal   Why does nobody believe me? I've told you once, I don't get off on that stuff!

Dr Kahn   But you know people who do?

Cal   Course I do!

Dr Kahn   You never have?

Pause.

Cal   Once. Years ago. It made me throw up. I hate throwing up.

Dr Kahn   Cal when you have these blackouts, do you ever get any warning beforehand?

Cal   Never.

Dr Gallagher   So you have had them before?

Cal   Does it matter?

Dr Gallagher gives Dr Kahn a look.

Scene 6 *(Internal): Children's ward*

Jack   Are you feeling any better?

Philip nods.

Jack   You could have lost your arm, you know. What were you doing, messing about with fireworks at your age? Some fool went in and bought 'em for you?

Philip   No.

Jack   Oh, you bought 'em yourself?

Philip says nothing.

Jack   I nearly lost a leg during war . . . You live down Grosvenor Place don't you?

Philip   Creswell.

Jack   Creswell? I used to know a chap ran the newsagent's down there. Opposite the park in't it?

Philip   No, next to the launderette.

Jack   Come October, he had a belting stack of fireworks – rockets, Catherine wheels, jumping jacks. . .

Philip   He gives you a book of transfers with every packet of bangers, he's great.

Jack pretends not to have any special interest.

Jack   Is that right?

Philip stays quiet, realising he's said too much already. Jack gives Philip a chocolate bar and exits.

We see Cal walking down the ward, his usual confident self. He passes Philip and catches sight of Lee.

Cal   You new?

Lee   Ish. I've just come from another ward.

Cal   Can't have been as boring as this dump.

Lee   Don't bet on it!

Pause.

Cal   Like a bet, do you?

Lee   Not especially, I just. . .

Cal   Fancy a game of summat?

Lee   Five a side if you're offering.

Cal   You don't look fit enough. I think there's an old Trivial Pursuit somewhere. You up to that?

Lee   Bit tame. Mind you we ran a Triv. tournament at school. I got as far as the second leg. Not bad for a starter.

Cal	Whoa! If you're one of these experts, forget it.
Lee	I din't say that. Anyway, I'll go easy on you, promise.
Cal	Nah, I'm out of cash anyway.
Lee	What do you need money for?
Cal	Pointless playing otherwise. Tell you what, I'll chuck this in for stakes.
	Lee is a bit stunned.
Lee	A Walkman? I've got nothing to match it.
	Cal picks up Lee's autographed ball from his bedside cabinet.
Cal	'Bout this?
Lee	Over my dead body!
	Lee snatches it back.
Lee	Signed by the entire Man. United team last year.
Cal	OK. Call it a fiver and you're on. Hang on there.
	Bryony anxiously reminds James that he is holding Cal's pack of Trivial Pursuit cards. James urgently leaps out from behind the curtains surrounding Bryony's bed and throws Cal's card pack back in his locker. Cal emerges round the corner a split second after this, startled by James.
Cal	What're you doing there?
James	Waiting for you. Where've you been?
Cal	A jog! Mind your own business.
	Cal reaches into his locker and grabs his Trivial Pursuit set, including card pack.
James	I want a return match.
	Cal is smug.
Cal	Missing your Walkman?
James	We wondered - me and Darren, that is - if you'd have the bottle to take us both on.
	Cal pretends to be scared.
Cal	You kidding? Bit one sided, init?

He pretends to consider.

Cal Depends what the stakes are?

James Darren's Pac-Man, my calculator and a New Kids album. You stake my Walkman, Darren's soccer boots and that money you're about to win off the other lad.

Cal Done. When?

James Tomorrow, three o'clock. In the boiler room.

Cal No can do. I've to go for tests tomorrow. Today, four on the dot.

He ruffles James' hair.

Cal See you, titch.

Cal exits.

James Hang on. . .

Darren's head springs out of the curtains. He hisses at James.

Darren Not today, you div!

James He said today.

Darren   We'll never learn the cards in time.

Bryony is in the background.

Bryony You won't if you stand there arguing.

Scene 7 *(External): Hospital grounds*

Keely is helping hospital voluntary workers to set out chairs and decorate a podium for the Lady Mayoress to sit on during the bonfire celebration. She is just reorganising the chairs to her own satisfaction when Billy, her boyfriend and father of her baby, appears. Billy studies the preparation.

Billy This is great. We never had bommies like this round our end. I'm getting excited already.

Keely Ah, does Billy want some sparklers then?

Billy laughs.

Billy Me gran used to make a massive hotpot for me and me mates - with red cabbage.

Keely   Hey look, if you're that keen to enjoy the food, you can give me a hand with the toffee apples later.

Billy   You're kidding? Can I?

Keely   Sister Meadows won't mind us both using the kitchen.

Billy   With the door shut?

He jokily moves in for a kiss. Keely laughs.

Keely   Cut it out, they're all watching.

Billy   So?

Keely   And we're behind schedule. We need some crates of drinks bringing down from the canteen. You can work up a sweat on that.

They start to move off.

Billy   Oh yeah, I nearly forgot.

He hands her a letter from his pocket.

Keely   Where's this from?

Billy   The flat. I nipped round there after work to see if the wallpaper had dried out all right.

Keely is mildly perturbed at this.

Keely   The flat? How did you get in?

Billy   Key. I had a set cut when I'd to wait in for the Gas Board. Well it's stupid us only having one set. Besides, when you decide you want me to move in with you, I'll need a set of me own, won't I?

She registers dismay at this, but it is not the time to take it into debate. She tears open the envelope and reads the letter.

Billy   Important?

Keely reads the letter.

Keely   They want me to go for a scan.

Billy is concerned.

Billy   What does that mean?

Keely   It's routine. Just to make sure the baby's all right. Bit like an X-ray without the X-ray.

Billy	When is it?
Keely	Nineteenth.
Billy	I'll book a day off, come with you.
Keely	It's all right, I can go on me own.
Billy	Yeah, but you know what that doctor said: the more I'm involved, the less pressure there is on you.

We see that Keely feels overcrowded.

Scene 8 *(Internal): Children's ward*

Around Danny's mattress plates and canteen hardware go crashing to the ground, splashing soup down Nurse Mags' uniform and over the floor. Mrs Phillips looks embarrassed. Nurse Grahams is a witness in the background.

Nurse Mags	You asked for soup.
Danny	I did not!

Sister Meadows approaches.

Sister Meadows	What's going on?
Nurse Mags	He chucked his dinner at me because he 'can't stand soup'. Look at the mess. If you weren't stuck in bed with that leg, I'd make you clear that up.
Danny	You wouldn't. You wouldn't 'coz it's not my fault. I didn't mean it.
Nurse Mags	You threw it. How could you not mean it?
Mrs Phillips	I have to say, he's not keen on soup.

Nurse Mags is shocked at this.

Nurse Mags	That's no excuse, Mrs Phillips – look at the state of me!

Sister Meadows remains calm and quiet.

Sister Meadows	Go and tidy yourself, up Nurse Mags. And calm down. Nurse Peters, would you see to this mess?

Nurse Mags storms off, followed by Nurse Grahams with the intention of giving her moral support.

*Nurse Mags indicates that she does not want
bothering. Dr Woods comes on to the ward, tracing
the source of trouble to Danny's bed. She sees the
mess and gathers what has happened.*

Dr Woods   Danny?

Scene 9 *(Internal): Ward office*

Sister Meadows   This is really bugging me. Danny's old enough to
know better. What's it all about?

Nurse Grahams enters.

Nurse Grahams   Can I say something?

Sister Meadows   What is it, Nurse Grahams?

Nurse Grahams   Well Danny's mood swings – sleeplessness,
general hyper-activity . . . I'm only saying
because we did it in school last week. And Dr
Whatsit from St Mary's reckons a dose of that
stuff can be like hard drugs to someone who's
allergic.

*Dr Woods is amused. She addresses Sister
Meadows.*

Dr Woods   Was that in English or is it me?

Sister Meadows speaks to Nurse Grahams.

Sister Meadows   Let's say that was a rehearsal.

Nurse Grahams   Well, have you considered Tartrazine and all that?

Dr Woods   'And all that' was dealt with last year.

Sister Meadows   Very good, Nurse Grahams. But Danny was sent
to a food allergy specialist by the family doctor.
It's in his notes.

Dr Woods   And, with respect, all those symptoms could fit a
hundred different conditions. . .

Nurse Grahams   Wait. That's just it. He didn't go.

Dr Woods   What do you mean?

Nurse Grahams   I've been reading up on his file for my case study.
The GP referred them but they never turned up
for the appointment.

Dr Woods	Are you sure? I'm sure I read the consultant's report.
Nurse Graham	No, there isn't one because they never went. Check it yourself.

Dr Woods and Sister Meadows share a glance - is it a possibility?

Scene 10 *(External): Council estate*

Jack is on his pushbike, circumnavigating a council estate's parade of shops. As he draws to a stop, his eyes narrow on a newsagent's next to the launderette, without doubt the shop Philip was describing. He pitches up opposite the shop, seeing a couple of kids, aged about twelve, coming out, wearing school uniform.

Scene 11 *(Internal): Newsagent's*

The newsagent is young and a bit of a wide boy, a big talker. A woman has taken a video to the counter.

Newsagent	I don't sell fireworks to kids, you must be mistaken.
Jack	I stood outside and watched 'em. Just now. Two of 'em buying bangers.
Newsagent	Look, it's not always cut and dried.

He speaks to the women.

Newsagent	Kids these days can look sixteen, no problem.
Jack	Give over – no more than twelve the pair of them. In school uniform.

He speaks to the women.

Jack	You passed 'em coming in.

The women start taking Jack seriously.

Jack	I've just come from hospital. Young lad this high. Scarred for life because of this . . . this baboon.

The newsagent forcefully pushes Jack to the door.

Newsagent	That's it, out!
Jack	You'll get nicked for this!
Newsagent	And you'll get what's coming if you don't shut your mouth. Right?

He pushes Jack out of door and tries to return casually to his business behind the counter.

Newsagent   *Evening News* was it, Linda?

But Linda and the other woman turn on their heels and exit the shop without buying, leaving a smell of boycott behind them.

Jack is sitting on the doorstep. The two women take off up the street. The newsagent storms out to confront Jack.

Newsagent   What the hell are you trying to do?

Jack   Obvious, in't it? Tell your customers what a nice chap you are. Any luck, we'll have you bankrupt by weekend.

Newsagent   You think they'll take any notice of you?

Jack watches the women disappear into the distance.

Jack   They did.

The newsagent finally snaps.

Newsagent   All right, all right, what do you want?

Jack   I want you to act with the common sense you were born with. No more fireworks to kids.

Pause.

Newsagent   Fine.

Jack   I want your word.

The newsagent answers through gritted teeth.

Newsagent   I promise.

Jack gets to his feet and dusts himself down.

Jack   Not that I trust you. But I'll be keeping me eye on you. Step out of line, I'll have the police on your doorstep.

Scene 12 *(Internal): Boiler room*

A crowd, including James, Darren, Lee, Philip and Rowena are bustling and gossiping. All go silent as Cal enters with his Trivial Pursuit box of tricks, surprised to find it bustling and gossiping.

Cal What's this?

Rowena 'Moral support'.

She turns to Lee.

Rowena Is that right?

Lee Dead right.

Cal Maybe I've missed a trick.

Cal sits down, trying hard not to look put off, bemused.

Cal Could've charged on the door.

Lee I've got a season ticket so count me out.

Pause.

James Right then.

Cal Right then. . .

Lee sets up the board, helped by Philip, and gets out the two boxes of cards. Cal leans over and adjusts the table, careful to put the marked box on their side. Lee turns a blind eye to this.

Lee How do you want to play it?

Darren We'll answer alternate questions when we get a move. Lee's playing referee.

Cal Do I get first dice since I'm solo. I'm feeling a bit – you know – intimidated, if that's what they call it.

Cal is lying.

Lee Sure.

Cal shakes.

Cal Three.

He moves three.

Cal Blue.

Lee Which European country's flag has stripes of red, white and green?

Cal Is it Germany?

Lee No, Italy.

Cal feigns disappointment.

Cal I thought I knew that.

Darren shakes.

Darren Five.

He moves five.

Darren Pink.

Lee Which bunch of kids have a computer called Ralph?

Darren Whizz-kids.

Lee Correct.

James shakes.

James Four.

He moves nine.

James Green.

Lee What day of the year do Britain's pyrotechnic displays take place on?

James panics.

James Pyro what?

Lee Have to time you . . . Answer is?

James shrugs.

Lee and Darren Bonfire night.

Darren They call fireworks pyrotechnics.

James How was I supposed to know!?

Smug Cal shakes again.

James being nudged by Darren as Cal shakes again.

Scene 13 *(Internal): Cafeteria*

Nurse Mags is eating alone, not enjoying her food or her day. As a couple of student nurses leave the table next to her, she catches sight of Mrs Phillips looking for a seat. The moment is embarassing. Mrs Phillips sheepishly takes the only seat available, opposite Nurse Mags. They eat in silence for a while.

Mrs Phillips   Trifle nice, was it?

Nurse Mags abandons her trifle. Nurse Mags speaks quietly and calmly.

Nurse Mags   I'd like to say something to you now. I'm speaking as a mother of three, so forget the uniform for a minute. I wasn't strict – too much the opposite, me mother used to say . . . But then, it's nigh on impossible to satisfy observers because they're not going through it, are they?

Mrs Phillip is stunned.

Nurse Mags   What I mean is . . . I know what it's like, I know there's no formula – quiet telling off works on Tuesday, but you've to resort to slap hands on Thursday. I know how hard it is, believe me.

She forces Mrs Phillips to square eyes.

Nurse Mags   But have you ever thought of your role in all this, Mrs Phillips? You're not doing him any favours, keeping siding with him, you know. Danny's obviously got a problem that needs seeing to. But you keep ignoring it. You'll have to get a grip, not just for Danny's sake, but the rest of us – you included.

She stands and pushes her chair in.

Nurse Mags   And what's more, I'm telling you now, if he refers to me as 'fatso' again, I'll sling his soup over his head.

Nurse Mags gets up and goes, leaving Mrs Phillips gobsmacked.

Scene 14 *(Internal): Ward office*

Mrs Phillips storms up to office door and barges in.

Mrs Phillips   I wish to make a complaint. . .

She finds Dr Woods with company – a tall, eccentric-looking woman in her forties, Dr Morris.

Dr Woods   Mrs Phillips. This is Bev Morris.

Dr Morris   How do you do.

Dr Woods   Dr Morris is a specialist in food-related allergies. We've asked her to investigate that possibility with Danny.

Mrs Phillips   Why?

Dr Morris   On Danny's records, Nurse Grahams noticed you tried something along these lines once before?

Mrs Phillips is not keen on the idea.

Mrs Phillips   Well, it cropped up. . .

Nurse Grahams   But you didn't turn. . .

Dr Morris signals Nurse Grahams to keep silent.

Dr Morris   Very sensible, too. With Danny's history, it was a very wise option. Some people dismiss the consequence of food on behaviour as inconsequential, Mrs Phillips. Often at their peril.

This tactic amuses Dr Woods.

Dr Woods   With your permission, we'd like to start cutting out certain foods, then introducing them back gradually.

Nurse Grahams   It's called an elimination diet.

Dr Morris looks to Sister Meadows, clearly needing Nurse Grahams out of the way for now. Sister Meadows ushers Nurse Grahams to the door.

Sister Meadows   Thanks, Nurse Grahams.

Dr Morris   The truth of it is that the obvious foods – cheese, chocolate – are well known to affect people with, say, migraine. But some triggers are far more subtle. The only way to track them down is to put them to the test. We'd like to cut Danny's diet down to basics and start from scratch.

Mrs Phillips feels press-ganged.

Mrs Phillips If you think it's going to help.

Dr Morris steers Mrs Phillips towards the door.

Dr Morris It certainly won't do any harm, let's put it that way. Look, why don't we have this conversation with Danny. I've got a feeling he'll appreciate being involved.

They start to go.

Sister Meadows Sorry, Mrs Phillips . . . What was the complaint?

Mrs Phillips Oh. . .

She has been sidetracked and signals to say 'forget it'. They go. Dr Woods turns to Sister Meadows with a smile. Sister Meadows smiles back.

Scene 15 *(Internal): Boiler room*

Tension is mounting. It is Cal's turn to shake.

Cal Six.

Moves twelve.

Cal Orange.

Lee What fraction of a mile is a 440-yard race?

Cal is shocked – it's the wrong question.

Cal Erm. . .

He doesn't know. He whispers.

Cal Shut it, will you!

He hazards a guess.

Cal Half. Half a mile.

Lee Nope. Quarter.

Cal snatches the card to check the answer. He looks with panic to his box of questions, wondering what has gone wrong. Darren throws the dice and moves.

Darren	Pink for a cheese!
Rowena	Take your time Darren.
Cal	Hey, schtumm!
Lee	Which pop singer has the nickname Alf?
Darren	Alison Moyet.
Lee	Correctimoso!
Crowd	Yes!
	Applause. It is James' turn to throw.
James	Four.
	He moves four.
Lee	Is it the last move? Is it the last question?
Philip	Come on, James.
Lee	Cal picks your colour.
	Cal chooses maliciously.
Cal	Green.
	James tuts.
Lee	Which went into space first – a dog, a cat, or a man?
	Long tense pause. Neither James nor Darren can remember.
Cal	Set the clock, Lee.
Lee	Speed it up chaps. Your opponent's losing weight over here. . .
	Cal is desperate by now.
Cal	Belt up!
Darren	Just guess.
James	A dog.
Lee	It's . . . Yes!!!
	He throws the card in the air. There is jubilation. Cal is shocked.
James	We won! We did it!
	He speaks to Cal.
James	Well slaughtered.

Pats on the back all round.

Lee Can I have me money back?

James answers jokingly.

James I'll play you for it.

James, Darren, Lee and Philip leave the room in celebration. The room has emptied now, but for Cal and Rowena. Cal sits stunned, facing Rowena.

Rowena I'm a bad loser, too. When Jessica Smith got in the dance team, I just wanted to do something bad.

She drifts off as she remembers.

Rowena I had a dream about cutting her uniform up. Her uniform always fits her really well round the waist. Mine looks good, but hers looks . . . better. I remember when. . .

Cal Rowena.

Rowena What?

Cal Not a good time. Yeah?

This is an understatement! She takes the point and leaves. The minute Cal is left alone, he pounces on his question pack to see what went wrong. He files through his cards, checking the front, checking the back. His face drops as it dawns on him that he has been setup.

Scene 16 *(Internal): Children's ward*

Dr Woods, Mrs Phillips and Dr Morris are at Danny's mattress.

Danny Why can't I have my orange juice?

Mrs Phillips We've explained, Danny.

Dr Morris patiently shows him the label of his cordial.

Dr Morris All these numbers . . . they're called additives . . . food colourings . . . not natural.

Danny	I like 'em.
Mrs Phillips	Danny!
Dr Morris	And these. . .

She points to a bag of crisps.

Dr Morris	And these. . .

She points to a packet of sweets.

Dr Morris	We want you to manage without them for a time to see if it makes you feel better. You do want to feel better, don't you, Danny?

Danny does not respond.

Dr Morris	Yes, of course you do.

She hands him an exercise book.

Dr Morris	No one else writes in this book but you. Each time you eat anything, I want you to describe how the food makes you feel. You'll do that for me, won't you, Danny?

He nods and takes the book with some curiosity. He gives a half-smile.

Danny	I will if I can go to the bonfire.

Dr Woods casts a glance at guilty Mrs Phillips.

Scene 17 *(External): Sparkies grounds*

A crowd of patients, adults, kids and several nurses have gathered. An ambulance is in evidence, along with a fire service van with equipment. Nurse Mags and Nurse Grahams wheel out Danny's new wheelchair, adapted with a plank to support his leg, to the spectator area.

Danny	It's freezing! I'm freezing!
Nurse Mags	Stop chucking your blankets off, then.

She addresses Nurse Grahams.

Nurse Mags	I thought he was supposed to be improving?
Nurse Grahams	Give it a chance. It can take up to four days for the allergic stuff to get out of his system.

Nurse Mags   If he lives that long!

Scene 18 *(External): Sparkies grounds*

Cal   Was it you set me up?

Bryony smiles.

Bryony   Wasn't hard from the next bed. Wouldn't have been so noticeable if you'd changed your routine now and again. But you kept spouting the same old lines and coming back with more stuff than Dixons. And I kept thinking, 'I've heard that somewhere before.'

Cal does not respond. He just stares into space. (We should be aware that this could be a symptom of something serious, but Bryony is not.)

Bryony   Oh, come on, it's not that bad. What if you'd won three Walkmans?

He breaks out of the stare, a bit disorientated. He sees her expecting an answer.

Cal   What?

Bryony   You all right?

Cal gets to his feet and storms off.

Bryony   Cal!

She makes to pursue him but her wheelchair is not so adept on rough ground. Cal disappears.

Scene 19 *(Internal): Casualty*

Dr Gallagher arrives in the casualty waiting area and treatment room to be met by the young female casualty officer (Dr Tanya Davies).

Dr Tanya Davies   Where've you been? We've tried bleeping you twice.

Dr Gallagher   Got caught up on the ward.

Dr Davies presents him with a file.

Dr Tanya Davies   Six-month-old male with blood streaked stools

	and colic.
Dr Gallagher	X-ray?
Dr Tanya Davies	Booked. Ten minutes.

They go into the treatment room where Gail Bevans and her infant son are waiting.

Dr Gallagher	Hello, Mrs. . .

He checks the chart.

Mrs Bevans	Bevans . . . What the hell's going on? We've been here 40 minutes and all we've had so far is people prodding and poking. He's in pain.
Dr Gallagher	I'm sorry about that, Mrs Bevans, but. . .
Mrs Bevans	I don't want excuses. Look at the colour of him.

Dr Gallagher moves closer for an examination.

Dr Gallagher	I'm gonna need to take some blood. Do you want to hold him?

Mrs Bevans picks young Jack up.

Dr Gallagher	Hello, Jack. I'm sorry if this hurts a bit, but we just want to know where we stand OK.
Mrs Bevans	Get on with it, please!

Dr Gallagher proceeds to take blood.

Scene 20 *(Internal): Casualty examination room*

Note: Baby Jack would now be attached to a glucose/saline infusion. Dr Davies is smiling.

Dr Tanya Davies	Mrs Bevan, we seem to have located what we think is the problem. Dr Gallagher. . .
Dr Gallagher	We've er . . . It looks like a condition we call intussusception. The lower bowel folds inside itself a bit like a telescope. Not uncommon in babies of Jack's age.
Mrs Bevans	Does that mean it needs an operation?

She dreads hearing 'yes'.

Dr Gallagher	Not if we can help it. I want to take him back down to X-ray for a barium enema. Sometimes

the pressure of the enema's enough to relieve the blockage. We'll need to move fairly fast while his fluid level's OK.

Mrs Bevan snaps back.

Mrs Bevans It could have been a lot faster if we hadn't been waiting so long.

Scene 21 *(External): Sparkies grounds*

Bryony Have you seen Cal?

Lee He'll be sulking somewhere. It was a brilliant match, you should have been there. What an atmosphere. Crowd roaring. Couple of off-sides and some pretty tight penalties, I can tell you. Cal lost everything. . .

As he turns round to face Bryony, she has already gone.

Bryony Nurse Mags!

Nurse Mags, in the distance, cannot hear her.

Bryony Darren! Where's Cal gone?

Darren does not hear. Bryony is thwarted.

Scene 22 *(External): Sparkies grounds*

Bryony is moving along in her wheelchair, virtually at waist-level to anyone standing.

Bryony Dr Woods. . .

Dr Woods Yes, Bryony?

Nurse Mags Dr Woods! Can Danny have Bonfire Toffee or not.

Dr Woods I'd prefer him not to. . .

Dr Woods heads towards Nurse Mags and Danny. Bryony is again thwarted. She has looked virtually everywhere. She stares into the shadows away from the bonfire. She tries to focus on the darkness. She thinks she may see something. She pursues her instincts.

Bryony   Cal?

She moves inside the shadows, getting wet soil and grass on her hands from pushing the wheels over rough ground. She wipes her hands down and focuses harder.

Bryony   Cal?

She goes round a corner where it's quieter, darker.

Bryony   Are you there?

Her face drops as her eyes adjust to a clearer picture. Cal is slumped on the ground, his limbs convulsing violently.

Episode Four
by Paul Abbott

Scene 1 *(External): Sparkies grounds*

Cal is in the throes of a convulsion. Bryony, alone with him, is shocked by the sight of him.

Bryony   Cal! Cal!

She struggles to get her wheelchair over the rough ground, close enough to the bonfire to make anybody hear her, but it is difficult for her.

Bryony   Help! Help!

Darren and some others are coming down the fire escape with a tray carrying extra goodies. They are laughing and joking. Bryony calls to them.

Bryony   Darren, get Dr Woods, or anybody.

Darren   What's the matter?

He catches sight of Cal. He is shocked.

Bryony   I don't know. Go. Go.

Darren races off towards the bonfire. Bryony looks down at Cal who gives one final convulsion, and lies still. Darren gets Nurse Mags' and Nurse Mitchell's attention. The music and general ribaldry drowns out what Darren says. Nurse Mags instantly looks around for Dr Woods who is busy chasing James around the bonfire in the distance. Nurse Mitchell races back with Darren towards Bryony.

Nurse Mags   Dr Woods.

Dr Woods sees the urgency on Nurse Mags' face and stops chasing James. Darren is with Bryony at top of the slope. Nurse Mitchell is with Cal, where seizure has now subsided. She has turned him into the recovery position, still unconscious. Nurse Mags, Nurse Grahams and Dr Woods arrive. Dr Woods quickly puts her stethoscope to Cal's chest.

Dr Woods   What happened?

Nurse Mitchell	Bryony found him in convulsion.
	She quickly examines external signs.
Dr Woods	Did he fall?
Nurse Mitchell	He was already down when I got here. Go back to the bonfire, Bryony.
	Bryony reluctantly moves away from the scene of the crisis, as instructed. Darren helps with the wheelchair. An ambulance with lights going comes round bend.

Scene 2 (*Internal*): *Children's ward*

The lift doors open. Dr Woods and Nurse Mitchell step out with ambulance crew. Cal is wheeled through to the ward where Dr Gallagher and Sister Meadows are now waiting. They place him in bed.

Dr Woods	Convulsion. Lacerations on impact. Bryony found him and Nurse Mitchell saw the tail-end of a seizure, but no one saw him collapse.
	She speaks to Nurse Mitchell.
Dr Woods	Bleep Dr Kahn.
	Nurse Mitchell moves away. Dr Woods speaks to Sister Meadows.
Dr Woods	I want him on neurological observations every thirty. And we'd better take a look at that cut.
Sister Meadows	I'll get the trolley.
	Sister Meadows moves away. Dr Woods gently runs her finger over Cal's eyelashes. Dr Gallagher's bleeper goes.
Dr Gallagher	That'll be the baby.
	He leaves.
Dr Woods	What baby. . .?
	Pause. There's *something* there.
	Sister Meadows tweaks Cal's ear lobe.
Sister Meadows	Cal, can you hear me? It's Sister Meadows. You're

back on the ward. Can you hear me?

Cal's eyes roll, open and start to focus.

Dr Woods Hello. Hello Cal. How are you?

Nothing.

Dr Woods You're back on the ward. You had some kind of seizure. How are you feeling?

Cal's eyes start to take in the scene. He scans his surroundings to orientate himself. He sees Nurse Mitchell smiling in his direction, clearly showing concern.

Scene 3 *(External): Sparkies grounds*

Bryony He didn't look like Cal, there on the floor. It was horrible.

Lee He'll be all right – they've got him upstairs now.

Bryony I shouldn't have had a go at him. I feel rotten now about setting him up – that game of Triv.

Lee Come on Bryony. That had nothing to do with it. He'd stitched up half the ward. He needed teaching a lesson.

Bryony cannot come to terms with this. Darren arrives, having just heard.

Darren What happened to Cal?

Bryony We 'taught him a lesson'.

She looks at Lee.

Lee That's not what I meant, you know it's not.

The bonfire is dying. Kids eat spuds. Rowena attempts to juggle with remaining potatoes.

Rowena What you have to do is, make sure you only concentrate on the ones you're catching. The rest of it comes naturally.

Philip picks one up off the floor and throws it to distract Rowena.

Rowena . . . Stop it. Nurse Mags, will you tell him?

Nurse Mags has Lucy asleep on her knee, dummy gyrating.

Nurse Mags To be honest, love, I haven't the energy.

She turns to nearby Nurse Grahams.

Nurse Mags I'll be glad when this lot are back in bed.

Nurse Grahams Oh, I could stay here all night. I love bonfires.

Nurse Mags So do I. But I want one of me own – wi' a casserole on it.

Nurse Grahams I met my first boyfriend at a bonfire. Steven McCormack. Big Prince fan. He had a T-shirt on saying 'If you love-heart love, love-heart somebody like me'.

Nurse Mags And did you?

Nurse Grahams No, he was too devious for a third year. Went for my best mate Jessica because her dad got free tickets for the cinema.

Nurse Mags I've come across a few of 'em like that.

She sees Billy taking Keely's hand, staring into the fire.

Nurse Mags Thank God there are enough of the other to keep romance in business.

Nurse Mitchell arrives.

Nurse Mitchell Can we start getting patients back upstairs now.

Nurse Mags stands, and picks up the megaphone.

Nurse Mags Right, you lot. Everybody from B1, single-file, right legs forward, on the march! Up the wooden hill.

James Do we have to?

Darren Just another half hour, Nurse Mags, please?

Nurse Mags I've got a home to go to. I'll count to five. One, two. . .

Scene 4 *(Internal): Baby ward*

Young Jack Bevans has been admitted to baby ward. The lights are dimmed. The night staff nurse adjusts drip to young Jack. Dr Gallagher listens with stethoscope for bowel sounds as Mrs Bevans looks on anxiously.

Dr Gallagher   All seems pretty sound down there.

Mrs Bevans   When will you know for sure?

Dr Gallagher   We'll hang on to him for 48 hours observation.

Mrs Bevans nods, registering fatigue.

Night Nurse   Why don't you get some sleep, Mrs Bevans?

Mrs Bevans is confused.

Mrs Bevans   I need to, er . . . I haven't brought any things. . .

Night Nurse   I can do you a clean nightie, a toothbrush and a cup of tea. How's that sound?

Mrs Bevans   Bliss, honestly!

She smiles for the first time The night nurse goes out. Mrs Bevans turns to Dr Gallagher. Her smile dissolves to acknowledge her disfavour with him.

Dr Gallagher   I'll be around if he needs me.

Dr Gallagher leaves.

Scene 5 *(Internal): Children's ward*

A new day. End-of-breakfast scene – Nurse Mags and Nurse Grahams are pulling in trays. Nurse Mags speaks to Danny's bed, cautiously.

Nurse Mags   Morning, Danny.

Danny mumbles something. Nurse Mags snaps at him!

Nurse Mags   What was that?

Danny   Have you read it?

He holds up the Beano annual. Nurse Mags is taken aback by his politeness.

Nurse Mags   Oh. No, I haven't.

Danny is trying very hard.

Danny   You can borrow it if you like. I saw you flicking through it yesterday. Have a read.

Nurse Mags   Thanks, Danny. It'll keep me company at break.

She adds pointedly.

Nurse Mags   Thanks very much.

Nurse Mags moves away to the trolley where Nurse Grahams is wiping Lucy's mouth.

Nurse Mags   Knock me over with a wet nappy! You wouldn't think he was the same lad.

Nurse Grahams   Touch wood, his diet's working. Eliminate additives, eliminate aggro.

Nurse Mags   Hang about it's not *forced* to be that, is it? Danny's had enough tellings off to make him think twice about his behaviour. And, more to the point, so's his mum.

Scene 6 *(Internal): Lee's bed*

Lee is surrounded by Darren, James and Philip. His pyjama jacket is raised, showing them his scar.

Darren   Uugh! How many stitches?

Lee   Twenty-three.

James   I thought our Brian had a lot with ten.

Nurse Langdon arrives. He jokes with Lee.

Nurse Langdon   Put it away, Jones! It's not a trophy.

Lee   Wait till I'm in the showers after soccer.

Nurse Langdon reacts to this with concern.

Lee   I could earn a fortune with this. '10p a bash – how many stitches?'

James   Twenty-three at a guess.

Lee   First prize to the kid with the scouse accent! Well done.

Lee is aware that his football talk has aroused Nurse

*Langdon's concern. He smiles at him. Nurse Langdon
does not reciprocate, but just starts setting up the
dialysis machine, plugging it in, preparing the sterile
attachments.*

Philip   What do they call that again?

Nurse Langdon A dialysis machine. Cleans the blood like his
                   kidneys would if he had them.

                   He continues pointedly for Lee's benefit.

Nurse Langdon They haven't invented one for the brain, yet, but
                   I'm working on it.

Scene 7 *(Internal): Baby ward*

*Dr Gallagher arrives a bit flustered. Mrs Bevans is
just putting young Jack, (still attached to an
infusion), back down in his cot.*

Dr Gallagher   Hiya. Sorry, I know I said I'd pop in earlier, but I
                   was writing up notes till three.

Mrs Bevans   That's all right. Seems to be your style.

Dr Gallagher   Yeah, well. . .

                   He indicates Jack.

Dr Gallagher   I got no call-outs, so I reckoned he must've been
                   all right in the night.

Mrs Bevans   He took a feed at six and, touch wood, we've had
                   no problems.

Dr Gallagher   Great stuff.

                   *He moves to Jack, checks his abdomen with
                   stethoscope. Mrs Bevans is embarassed.*

Mrs Bevans   Dr Gallagher, I'm sorry. My attitude last night, I
                   was . . . when he fell sick, I thought I'd lost him. I
                   really am grateful for all you did. You were great
                   with him.

Dr Gallagher   Forget it. And thanks. . .

Hannah   Mummy!

                   *Mrs Bevans swings round to find Hannah, her
                   daughter, peeping round the door. She runs to*

	sweep her up.
Mrs Bevans	Hello, sweetheart!
	She hugs her.
Mrs Bevans	Oh, it is nice to see you.
	Mrs Bevans' mum, Esther, appears round door.
Mrs Bevans	Mum.
Esther	She wouldn't wait for me.
	She dumps a bag of goodies.
Esther	How is he?
Mrs Bevans	He's fine.
	She speaks to Hannah.
Mrs Bevans	Your brother's fine now. We'd no need to be so worried, had we? Look he's smiling at you. What do you say?
Hannah	Jack Spratt!
	A catch phrase.
Dr Gallagher	I'll leave you to it.
Mrs Bevans	Oh, I'm sorry. Mum, this is Dr Gallagher. He's been looking after us. Doctor, this is Hannah.
Hannah	I've got a sore finger.
Mrs Bevans	No you haven't. He's getting all the attention for once.
Dr Gallagher	Catch you later.
	He goes. Esther is a heavy scrutineer.
Esther	Bit under-dressed for a doctor.
Mrs Bevans	They don't all hide behind three-piece suits these days, you know.
Esther	Looks like he's just got out of bed to me.
	She turns quickly to Jack.
Esther	Who's a healthy boy, then? Who's going to smile for his grandma?

Scene 8 *(Internal): Cal's bed*

Nurse Mitchell opens the curtains from around Cal's bed, having just done his neurological test.

Nurse Mitchell Sure you've finished?

Cal Sure.

He watches Nurse Mitchell go with his untouched tray. Then he catches Bryony looking his way. He stays flat on his back, staring at the ceiling, refusing to meet her eyes.

Bryony Are you all right now?

Cal Fine, why?

Bryony Last night. You frightened me.

Cal Did you see it?

Bryony You were flat out. What *is* the matter, do you know?

Cal Who else saw it? Who else knows?

Bryony Nobody, I only. . .

Cal finally pierces her with a glare.

Cal Well keep it that way, eh? It didn't happen, right?!

Bryony Yeah, but. . .

He turns away again and closes his eyes. Nurse Mitchell returns to Cal's bed with a wheelchair, his notes under her arm.

Nurse Mitchell Come on, Cal. Time for your appointment.

Cal You can ditch that for a start. I'm going nowhere in a wheelchair.

Nurse Mitchell I'm sorry, I'm not prepared to accompany you unless you go in a chair. What if you pass out again?

Cal Leave me where I am.

Sister Meadows arrives.

Sister Meadows What's the matter?

Nurse Mitchell He won't use the chair.

Sister Meadows	I wish you would, Cal.
	Cal remains stubborn.
Cal	Second wish?
Sister Meadows	Keep a close eye on him.
	Cal swings himself off the bed and struts on ahead. Nurse Mitchell indignantly follows behind with his notes.

Scene 9 *(Internal): Hydrotherapy pool*

Bryony, in swimwear, is having her legs manipulated by the physiotherapist.

Physio	You're not concentrating.
Bryony	It hurts.
Physio	You know it does at first.
	He continues emphatically.
Physio	You also know that it always feels better after your exercise, so come on. Use the water to take your weight. Bend.
	Bryony forcefully kicks herself off and escapes across to the other side of the pool, with a laugh, letting the water take her.
Physio	That's not what you're here for.
	Bryony bobs head first into the water, anarchically enjoying the freedom. As she rises to the surface again, the physio has swum to catch her.
Bryony	All right.
	Exercises proceed again.
Physio	What's on your mind?
Bryony	This place. It's all right when you know the routine. But it must do their head in when they don't want to be here.
Physio	Nobody wants to be in hospital.
Bryony	You know what I mean – really hate being here.

Scene 10 *(Internal): Children's ward*

Dr Woods is speaking to Sister Meadows, Steve and Dr Gallagher.

Dr Woods   Dr Morris wants us to introduce the testers on Danny Phillips.

She indicates over to Danny's bed where his Mum is playing draughts with him.

Dr Woods   And since she's quietly confident that Tartrazine is the gremlin, we should start with that.

Steve Bailey   What if he hits the roof?

Dr Woods   He will if we're successful. It's if nothing happens you start worrying. Because it means we've to start over again.

Steve Bailey   Does his mum know?

Dr Woods   I'd rather she didn't.

Dr Woods moves to Danny's bed and joins Mrs Phillips and Danny. Dr Woods flicks through Danny's personal diary.

Dr Woods   Well done, Danny. You've really made an effort with your diary.

He smiles.

Dr Woods   One – fish makes you tired. Was that just yesterday or does it happen all the time?

Danny   Just yesterday.

Mrs Phillips   He usually likes fish, don't you?

Danny   Especially sardines. On toast.

Dr Woods   Well, hopefully, it won't be long before you're back on a full diet. OK?

Danny   Great.

Dr Woods moves away down the ward, signalling to Nurse Mags and Nurse Grahams, who are dishing out jugs of water. Nurse Mags, on Dr Woods prompt, takes a glass of orange cordial from the trolley and casually takes it to Danny's bedside locker, along with his jug of water.

Nurse Mags	There you go, love.
Mrs Phillips	Erm . . . I thought Doctor said he wasn't allowed?
Nurse Mags	Oh, it's fine now. Doctor says it's fine.

Nurse Mags moves away, casually as possible, quietly signalling her trepidation to Nurse Grahams. She is now a safe distance away.

Nurse Mags	I think they're mad. What if he throws another screeching tantrum?
Nurse Grahams	Bingo!

Nurse Mags and Nurse Grahams both look round in time to see Danny taking a swig of his orange cordial. Nurse Mags speaks with great apprehension.

Nurse Mags	You can clear this away.

She indicates the trolley.

Nurse Mags	I've got appointments in the dayroom.

Nurse Mags moves away. We see Danny who is oblivious to the debate surrounding him.

Scene 11 *(Internal): Neuorology unit*

Cal is in a chair, having electrodes attached to his head by a technician. Nurse Mitchell is sitting in the corner, observing. The technician finishes fixing the last.

Technician	Does that feel comfortable?
Cal	I feel a nerd.

The technician moves to the machine.

Technician	Now, when I switch on, I'll give you simple instructions. If you could do your best to follow them. . .

He switches on. The pencil on the EEG graph activates. Cal swings round to see what is happening.

Technician	No, keep still. Relax and close your eyes.

He does and the graph reacts.

Technician Open.

Cal does so and stares at Nurse Mitchell opposite.

Technician Close again.

We see the pencil line as it peaks and troughs its way through yards of paper. We see Cal trying to concentrate.

Scene 12 *(Internal): Neurology unit corridor*

Cal and Nurse Mitchell emerge from the EEG room. Nurse Mitchell has a copy of the EEG results graph. She folds it inside his file and proceeds to lead the way back.

Cal What does it say, Mitch?

Nurse Mitchell It doesn't say anything. And please don't call me that.

Cal What does it show then?

Nurse Mitchell is tolerant. She stops walking briefly.

Nurse Mitchell It shows examples of how your brain waves are functioning. The different stages of the graph represent a different wave. If you really wanted to know, you should have let Dr Kahn explain it to you properly.

She sets off again. Cal pursues her.

Cal What do mine say?

Nurse Mitchell I don't know, I'm not a doctor.

Cal You know enough, though, don't you?

Nurse Mitchell Dr Kahn will examine them later and discuss them with you. That's his job.

Cal So why did they make me have it? What do they think it'll tell 'em?

She ignores him.

Cal Come on, Mitch.

He dashes in front of her, walking backwards to obstruct her face.

Cal   I want to know. It's my brain they've been looking at, I want to know before we get back.

He stops her dead.

Cal   Please.

This appeal touches her. It exposes his vulnerability, his desperate fear, which takes her aback.

Nurse Mitchell   To investigate the possibility of epilepsy.

His face drops, stunned.

Cal   Where does it say that?

Nurse Mitchell   I've told you, I don't know that it says that. . .

He snatches the file, and the graph, unravelling it violently.

Nurse Mitchell   Cal!

Cal   Where does it say that!? This is all bull! They make it up.

He starts tearing up the graph, avoiding her hands.

Cal   They . . . make . . . it . . . up!

Nurse Mitchell   This is outrageous!

. . . Cal legs it, as fast as he can down the corridor, turning the corner. She scoops up the shreds and files, and heads off after him.

Nurse Mitchell   Cal!

Scene 13 *(External): Sparkies grounds*

Cal is running hell for leather in his pyjamas and dressing gown, through the grounds. An ambulance on its way to casualty has to swerve to avoid him. He legs it through the first door that looks available.

Scene 14 *(Internal): Hospital chapel*

Cal surges through the door, shocked to find himself faced with the altar of a hospital chapel and stained glass windows. He takes a seat and gets his breath back, sinking his head in his hand to escape the situation. The door swings open and Nurse Mitchell appears. She moves gently towards him and sits down at his side. Cal lifts his head.

Cal At first, I didn't know what was happening. Just now and again, I'd drift off – on the bus on the way to school. People had been talking to me without me realising.

Pause.

Cal Then it happened at home in me bedroom. When I came round, my nose was bleeding where I'd banged it. And I'd bit me lip.

Nurse Mitchell But you didn't tell anyone?

Cal No chance.

Nurse Mitchell Cal, it's nothing to be ashamed of. The seizures are a kind of electrical storm in the brain, like a thunder. . .

Cal is preoccupied with his own thoughts.

Cal Digger.

Nurse Mitchell I'm sorry?

Cal Lad in our class who used to have fits. We called him Digger. 'Coz every time he threw a wobbler, we reckoned he looked like he could dig a road up.

He laughs sardonically.

Cal He stopped coming to school in the end.

Nurse Mitchell I'm not surprised! Haven't your parents noticed anything?

Cal Oh sure. Me room's a mess, I'm never home on time, and now and again, I rifle me dad's milkmoney for spends. But one day, I'm gonna

	take 'em by surprise, aren't I?
Nurse Mitchell	They'll be told now anyway. Dr Kahn will prescribe a course of treatment until your system can be balanced. When you go back to school, they'll be none the wiser.
	Cal stands. He is upset.
Cal	You don't understand! You haven't a clue! They trash you for anything round our end. They'll dig till they find out, I know they will. And come up with a name for me, no problem! 'Spaz', 'Squirmie'.
	He yells.
Cal	I hate it! I don't want it!
Nurse Mitchell	Cal. You can't control the way the idiots think. But you can face up to them.
	He looks at her.
Cal	Tell 'em? No chance!
Nurse Mitchell	Imagine how you would've taken it if 'Digger' had tried opening his heart to you.
	Cal shakes his head to dismiss the theory – it does not fit in with his culture. Nurse Mitchell stands.
Nurse Mitchell	Come on, we'd better get back before they send a search party.
	He stands to follow her.
Nurse Mitchell	I'd appreciate it if you'd do me a favour. I shouldn't have given you some of that information, so. . .
	He nods dolefully to acknowledge secrecy. They exit the chapel as Cal found it empty, just the stained glass windows boasting their silhouettes.

Scene 15 *(Internal): Ward office*

Nurse Mitchell and Cal arrive in the office

Sister Meadows	Where've you been? Dr Kahn's here.
Nurse Mitchell	We were delayed.

Sister Meadows	That's it? Delayed?
Nurse Mitchell	Delayed.

She hands over the EEG graph to Sister Meadows in shreds, (a bit tidied up since we last saw it). Sister Meadows just stares.

Nurse Mitchell	I'm afraid it got caught in the lift doors on the way back. I'm truly sorry about that.

Sister Meadows is a bit stunned.

Sister Meadows	Cal, Dr Kahn's in the interview room with your parents.

She adds pointedly.

Sister Meadows	She's been here half an hour.

Cal goes away. There's a pause in which Sister Meadows considers saying something to Nurse Mitchell, but frankly, cannot find the words. She follows Cal into the office. Nurse Mitchell proceeds to the kitchen counting her blessings.

Nurse Mitchell	Well we'd better go and see her then.

Scene 16 *(Internal): Children's ward*

Sister Meadows is at James' bed, supervising his self-injection, and at the same time, keeping a cautious eye on Danny. Rowena, in the background, has a Casio keyboard organ strapped round her neck, playing it badly. Sister Meadows cringes.

Sister Meadows	Where did she get her hands on that?
James	She asked her dad to bring it in for her.
Sister Meadows	Remind me not to book her for any parties.
James	Isn't she fit enough to be sent home. If it's not that thing, she's rabbiting everybody to death. Rabbit, rabbit, rabbit.
Sister Meadows	You don't do so bad yourself.
James	Yeah, but I usually make sense.

We see Rowena go down the ward. We move to

Darren's bed which is raised chest downward. The physio is pummelling the back of his chest to relieve fluid.

Darren Oh, I can't bear it! If her batteries don't run out soon, I'm gonna jump all over it.

The physio presents a sputum cup, into which Darren is expected to cough up excess.

Danny gives a piercing yell.

Danny Shut up!!!

Rowena stands rigid near Danny's bed as he screams.

Danny You can't play it so why do you try? It's like listening to chalk on a blackboard!

Mrs Phillips Danny!

Danny lobs one of his pillows in Rowena's direction. It misses, but Rowena, with the shock of it all, bursts into tears. Sister Meadows arrives.

Sister Meadows All right, Rowena. It wasn't really anything to do with you.

Rowena goes away. Sister Meadows speaks to Nurse Grahams.

Sister Meadows Clear his locker.

Nurse Grahams quickly shifts Danny's water jug and anything breakable as Dr Woods arrives from the office.

Mrs Phillips . . . I'm sorry, he was fine. He was just nodding off, then . . . Nurse Mags gave him orange juice, you know.

Dr Woods remains calm.

Dr Woods No problem, Mrs Phillips. Can I have a word in the office?

Danny Oh yeah, go on. Talk about me. Everybody goes in there to talk about me! Well ask me if I care!

He flings his bedding on to the floor and starts shaking his bed. Dr Woods guides a bewildered

Mrs Phillips to office. Sister Meadows smiles.

Danny What's *funny?*

We see a smiling group of kids and staff who have congregated to catch the spectacle.

James He's a nutter.

Scene 17 *(Internal): Ward office*

Dr Woods is now with Dr Gallagher, and Mrs Phillips, who blows her nose into a handkerchief. Steve observes.

Mrs Phillips I'm sorry. I just can't stand it. It's too much, all that time!

Dr Woods There's something we didn't tell you, Mrs Phillips. We expected this.

Mrs Phillips How? Why?

Dr Gallagher The orange juice.

Dr Woods corrects him.

Dr Woods Cordial. That particular cordial has a high proportion of additives.

Mrs Phillips You gave it to him deliberately? That just seems cruel. . .

Dr Gallagher Without testing it, we'd never have known what the problem was.

Dr Woods There's usually more than one food in the background, so we must continue testing.

Steve Bailey But in the meantime, Mrs Phillips, I'd like you to realise that we're all working together on this. It'll help if we follow the plan.

Mrs Phillips is somewhat contrite.

Mrs Phillips Of course.

She looks out of the window to Danny.

Scene 18 *(Internal): Children's ward*

Dr Woods is at Danny's bed with Danny and his mum. He has calmed down a bit. Sister Meadows finishes putting his bedding back in order.

Dr Woods   Not just orange juice. A lot of the sweets I've seen you buying – the cheaper ones especially – they contain lots of this stuff.

Mrs Phillips   It's the food colouring, Danny. It's been doing awful things to your system.

Danny   No it hasn't! I like 'em. I like orange juice.

Dr Woods   Well it's fresh orange juice only while you're in here. You can please yourself once you're home. But it would be very silly to ignore the results of these tests, wouldn't it?

Danny does not respond.

Scene 19 *(Internal): Children's ward*

Rowena is under the covers of her bed. Nurse Mags taps her on the shoulder.

Rowena   I don't want to talk to anybody.

Nurse Mags   Look what I've got.

Rowena emerges to find Nurse Mags with her Casio keyboard organ. Darren is standing there with a pair of earphones from his Walkman.

Darren   Watch.

He plugs in the earphones to the socket in the back of the organ. He plays a few bars and removes the earphones.

Darren   That was a bit from Paula Abdul. But you'd never guess 'coz nobody can hear it but you.

A look of relief dawns on Rowena's face. Darren proffers the earphones. She tries it. Rowena speaks loudly.

Rowena   Could you tell what that was?

Darren and **Nurse Mags**	No.
	Rowena takes off her earphones and smiles.
Rowena	Thanks, Darren.
Darren	My pleasure.
Rowena	I can play it as much as I want now.
	She puts her earphones back on and plays a few bars.
Darren	You owe me 50 pence. You said she'd never wear it.
	Nurse Mags whispers to Darren.
Nurse Mags	I'll pay you later.

Scene 20 *(Internal): Lee's bed*

Mrs Jones	I've missed you at home.
	Lee is embarassed.
Lee	Mam!
Mrs Jones	Well I have. I'd to put the bins out meself on Friday.
	Lee smiles and lets her take his hand.
Lee	Stick me CD on full blast; you'll never know I've gone.
	Mrs Jones laughs heartily.
Mrs Jones	Mind you, there isn't a stack of dirty plates.
	Pause.
Mrs Jones	I'll have to get back to work shortly.
	Lee checks the time.
Lee	Ah hang on. Few more minutes.
Mrs Jones	You see! You are missing your mum!
	She kisses Lee.
Lee	Shhh!

Scene 21 *(Internal): Hospital car park*

We see a row of cars facing the main door. Eddie Jones is sitting with his girlfriend Frances in her car – a C-registration Fiesta. Frances watches Mr Jones as his eyes stay anxiously transfixed on the main door. He checks the time, getting more impatient.

Frances Eddie. Is this a good idea? We could come back later.

Mr Jones He's my son. I've the right to speak to him when I like. I want to see him now.

This is not the first time she has appealed to him, nor the first time he has fought for his own way, determinedly. Frances looks distinctly uncomfortable, wishing she had never volunteered to drive him.

Scene 22 *(Internal): Main corridor/ward*

Cal's mum and dad are heading off down the corridor ad-libbing goodbyes. Cal moves back up towards the ward with Dr Gallagher. Sister Meadows and Nurse Mitchell are outside the office, starting medication rounds.

Dr Gallagher I'll catch you later, Cal.

Cal continues up to his bed.

Sister Meadows Well?

Dr Gallagher The EEG suggested temporal lobe epilepsy. Cal took it really well.

(To which Nurse Mitchell responds privately.)

Dr Gallagher Funny, init. Fear of losing control. You can stand outside any pub on a Saturday night and see grown men who don't know what day it is. For somebody like Cal, it'll take him years to come to terms with it.

Sister Meadows It will if he keeps dodging good advice.

Dr Gallagher	Kahn wants us to try him on Tegretol 200.

He opens Cal's file.

Dr Gallagher	I'll write it up and you can start him straight away.

Nurse Mitchell looks down at Cal, who gives her a very discreet wink. She returns it. We see Lee's mum making her exit.

Mrs Jones	Thanks Sister.
Sister Meadows	Our pleasure.
Mrs Jones	I'll try and nip back tonight but I've told him I'm not promising.
Sister Meadows	Bye.

Mrs Jones turns the corner and heads towards the lift.

Scene 23 *(External): Hospital car park*

Frances and Mr Jones are still in the car waiting. The radio is now on. His tensions are constantly being picked up by Frances. Mr Jones switches off the radio and focuses his eyes on the main door. Mr Jones sees Mrs Jones leaving the hospital. Mr Jones' scornful eyes follow her as she heads safely out of sight, round a corner. He springs into action and leaves the car.

Mr Jones	Are you coming?
Francis	I don't think that's wise, do you?
Mr Jones	I'm sick of playing games for her benefit. Lee knows we come as a pair.
Francis	He doesn't even like me.
Mr Jones	Only because she doesn't.
Francis	I'd rather not, Eddie. Really. . .

But he has already abandoned her and is heading for the main doors with determination.

Scene 24 *(Internal): Children's ward*

Lee is gently meandering down to the washroom with his toilet bag. He speaks to Nurse Mitchell as she passes.

Lee   Off to clean me teeth. All the grub in here tastes like fillings.

He speaks to Danny who is now without the protection of his mum.

Lee   That right, Rambo?

Danny replies innocently.

Danny   I don't know.

Danny has a look of vulnerability. He does not know why he is being 'got at'.

Scene 25 *(Internal): Main corridor*

Bryony is being brought back from the hydrotherapy pool by the physio, (both have damp hair). The physio parks her in the corridor whilst she reports to the office. Bryony mischievously disappears in her wheelchair. She hides herself in the recess beyond the payphone. Lee comes down ward and enters the corridor. He comes face to face with his dad.

Mr Jones   Lee.

Lee's hackles are raised.

Lee   I don't. . .

Mr Jones   Don't shout, don't slag me. Your mother's not here, so we can cut all that and keep it civilized.

He continues with the assumption that this carries weight.

Mr Jones   How are you? What've they said?

(Bryony, tucked away in her corner, was simply expecting a game of hide and seek with the physio. This terse exchange is far more than she bargained for.)

Mr Jones	. . .I've been worried sick about you.
Lee	Since when?

Mr Jones is a bit taken aback.

Mr Jones	What d'you mean, since when? Since I heard what you'd been through.
Lee	You've no. . .
Mr Jones	Don't tell me I've no right to be here. That's straight out of your mother's phrase book.
Lee	You're rich, you are! You said that last time you turned up – eleven months ago.
Mr Jones	Listen, that's because. . .
Lee	No! You come out with the same lines every time you turn up. 'Blame your mam for turning things sour.' 'We could've got along fine if it weren't for her'. 'I care about you, I really do.' Well, you know, I stopped believing that last year. I stopped believing it when you stopped turning up.
Mr Jones	I'm here. I'm here aren't I?
Lee	You're here because it'd look bad if you weren't! Mum doesn't tell me what to think. I make me own decisions now. And the best one I made was forgetting all about you, 'coz you're just not worth it. . .

Mr Jones grabs him in a reflex action, which causes Lee some pain – he winces. Mr Jones quickly draws away.

Mr Jones	Lee, I'm sorry. Sorry. Does it hurt?

Lee answers stubbornly.

Lee	No. . .

He recovers himself.

Mr Jones	What have they done to you? I want to know.
Lee	Ask Mum.

Lee walks away, back to the ward, leaving his toilet bag on the floor where it fell. Mr Jones' face registers bitter disappointment with himself for handling it badly. He speeds down the corridor and away. Bryony emerges from her hiding place, shocked and embarrassed to have been party to this incident. She picks up the toilet bag and heads for the ward. Sister Meadows comes from the office and crosses Bryony.

Sister Meadows   In bed, Mischief!

Bryony answers quietly.

Bryony   In a sec. . .

Scene 26 *(Internal): Children's ward*

Lee is at the window. He watches Frances and his dad pull away. Bryony intercepts Lee's rage.

Bryony   Sorry.

Lee spins round.

Lee   What?

She proffers the toilet bag.

Bryony   You dropped it.

Lee takes it, head down, hiding tears.

Bryony   Your dad?

Lee turns back to see Mr Jones' van disappearing out of view.

Lee   No. He's nothing. They don't exist!

His face melts helplessly to express his abject hurt.

Episode Five
by John Chambers

Scene 1 *(Internal): Hospital radio studio*

DJ starts his show in the style of Robin Williams.

DJ 'Good morning Sparkies!' Hope you're feeling better than me – I've got a frog in my throat so big I think I'm turning into a prince – talking of whom – here is Prince with 'Purple Rain'.

He takes a record from its sleeve and starts up the cassette deck.

DJ Or rather it will be when I get my record back. C'mon now. Own up. Who's nicked it? In the meantime, here's something completely different.

Scene 2 *(Internal): Rowena's bed*

Our of frustration Lee is kicking a bit of rolled-up newspaper. He is engrossed and, almost in slow motion, is enacting some goal he would like to score. Rowena, interrupts his dreams.

Rowena You and me might be at a Cup Final together one day. I think a lot of football teams are going to have cheerleaders like they do in America.

She does a chant and actions.

Rowena Two, four, six . . . three. Who's going to score – yes, it's Lee.

Lee The crowd'd go before the kick-off.

Rowena moves off, still chanting to herself. Lee kicks the paper and it lands at Nurse Langdon's feet. They do some mock dribbling. Unseen, Dr Gallagher arrives, he watches. Nurse Langdon sees Dr Gallagher and stops, embarrassed.

Dr Gallagher What d'you think you're doing?

Nurse Langdon Dr Gallagher . . . I was just er. . .

Dr Gallagher smiles.

Dr Gallagher You were just about to pass to me.

Lee takes the 'ball' from Nurse Langdon and dribbles up towards the office. Other kids, including Darren and James, cheer. Lee speaks to Nurse Langdon.

Lee You tuning up my super-dooper customised dialysis machine?

Nurse Langdon That's right – I might even put go-faster stripes on it.

Lee watches Nurse Langdon in the background. Nurse Mags, with a pillow case, goes down the ward – Dr Gallagher having just dribbled past her. Nurse Mags speaks to Nurse Grahams.

Nurse Mags Do they ever grow up?

Nurse Grahams looks, as though asking who.

Nurse Mags nods in Dr Gallagher's direction.

Nurse Mags Boys.

Nurse Grahams I know. . .

She gently lobs a pillow to Nurse Mags. Nurse Mags shakes her head and smiles.

Scene 3 *(Internal): Outside/inside ward office*

Dr Gallagher has to dribble past Jack who has just arrived with a trolley. Jack virtually spins his trolley round to avoid Dr Gallagher.

Jack I'd be safer in the fast lane of the M61 . . . Oh, Dr Gallagher, could I have a. . .

But Dr Gallagher has gone into the office where he interrupts Sister Meadows and a tight-lipped Nurse Mitchell. We see Jack hovering for a moment then he leaves.

Nurse Mitchell . . . after all it's not the first time . . .

Sister Meadows and Nurse Mitchell look at Dr Gallagher.

Dr Gallagher	Oh, sorry just keeping in shape in case Kenny Dalglish calls. What's up?
Sister Meadows	We were just talking about Nurse Grahams.
Dr Gallagher	Bright girl.
Nurse Mitchell	Have you seen her?
	Dr Gallagher nods.
Dr Gallagher	She's out on the ward.
Nurse Mitchell	Have you seen her?
Dr Gallagher	Is this a trick question?
Nurse Mitchell	Psychedelic hair and tights to match – again.
Dr Gallagher	I hadn't noticed.
	He glances at Sister Meadows.
Dr Gallagher	Does it matter?
Nurse Mitchell	I know we don't agree, Dr Gallagher, about what is and is not appropriate dress on this ward, but I think if the nursing officer were to hear of this, Nurse Grahams' future might be in some jeopardy – bright as she may be.
Dr Gallagher	Nurse Mitchell. I don't honestly believe. . .
	Sister Meadows interrupts him.
Sister Meadows	Thank you Nurse Mitchell. Could you give a hand with the beds.
	Nurse Mitchell exits and we leave with her. We can see Mrs Bevans and Lucy in the baby ward.

Scene 4 *(Internal): Baby ward*

Lucy, with dummy, is looking at Baby Jack who is asleep. Mrs Bevans tidies up one or two things and comes over to Lucy, puts her arm around her and also looks at Jack.

Mrs Bevans	Jack will be after your dummy.
Lucy	He can have it.
	She takes it from her mouth and is about to stick it in Jack's.

Mrs Bevans	No, it's all right really.
Lucy	I've got spare dummies, lots of them . . . You keep it. . .

Lucy puts the dummy back in her mouth as Keely enters.

Keely	There you are, Lucy. Are you coming to do some drawing?
Lucy	Yes.

She goes to leave.

Lucy	I'm going to draw Jack.

She goes out. Keely cannot resist taking a peep at Jack.

Keely	He looks bonny.

Mrs Bevans nods.

Mrs Bevans	Lot better than when he came in.
Keely	I'm glad he's all right. . .
Mrs Bevans	Be a day or two before we're sure whether it's worked, Dr Gallagher says.
Keely	It'll be OK – he's great Dr Gallagher.
Mrs Bevans	Yeah . . . when's yours due?

Scene 5 *(Internal): Children's ward*

Nurse Mags is coming down the middle corridor with some fresh linen. As she comes on to the ward, Danny and Cal are in the middle of an argument.

Cal	Get lost.
Danny	Give it to me.

Cal dangles a comic just out of Danny's reach.

Danny	Give it to me you rotten thief.
Cal	Temper, temper.

As Nurse Mags reaches them, Nurse Grahams is making her way up from the end of the ward. Nurse Mitchell is wheeling Bryony, in wheelchair, to her bed. (Sister Meadows is in the office on the phone, Dr Gallagher is in the baby ward with Mrs Bevans and Keely.)

Danny	I'll get you.
Nurse Mags	Ey, come on calm down.
Cal	He's a head-banger.
Nurse Mags	The pair of you!
Nurse Mitchell	What's the matter?
Danny	He nicked my comic.
Cal	I borrowed it.
Danny	Without asking. You just took it.

Cal knows he is in the wrong. He slings the comic at Danny, and goes off. Danny goes to pick it up. Nurse Grahams arrives and picks it up for him.

Nurse Mags	Ey, Danny, I thought we'd seen the last of this kind of thing.

Danny moves off, lamely, quiet.

Danny	He should have asked. . .

They move away.

Nurse Mitchell	He's keeping to his diet, I hope. No midnight feasts of sweets and things?
Nurse Mags	As far as I know.

Nurse Grahams joins them.

Nurse Grahams	He's all right.

Nurse Mitchell speaks to Nurse Grahams.

Nurse Mitchell	I hope you're keeping a very close eye on him. There's no point in running a control test if there's no control.
Nurse Grahams	He's all right!
Nurse Mitchell	What was all that about then?
Nurse Mags	That was a ten-year-old lad who was browned off because someone'd pinched his comic. That's all.
Nurse Mitchell	The boy lacks any real discipline.

Sister Meadows arrives from the office.

Sister   Nurse Grahams, could I have a word?

Nurse Grahams looks at Nurse Mitchell. They know what this is about. So does Nurse Mags, who sees this, her face registers her impatience with Nurse Mitchell. Nurse Mags moves over to Bryony to plump up her pillows, etc. Nurse Mitchell goes off towards Cal.

Scene 6 *(Internal): Cal's bed*

In the background Bryony adjusts her position and overhears the following.

Nurse Mitchell   It's not worth fighting over a comic, Cal. . .

Cal is about to protest. Nurse Mitchell raises her finger.

Nurse Mitchell   . . . Now is it?

Cal is about to react.

Cal   'E's a little . . .

Nurse Mitchell cuts in.

Nurse Mitchell   And you're old enough to know better.

Cal   If a teacher talked to me like you, I'd be straight out of that classroom.

Nurse Mitchell   You know where the door is.

Cal smiles.

Cal   It's cold outside.

Nurse Mitchell   So you're staying?

Cal nods.

Nurse Mitchell   Good, because I don't fancy chasing you all round South Park again. Or explaining to Sister Meadows where I disappeared to.

Cal   Half the staff here are two-faced. At least you're straight. Like over me . . .

He is aware of the possibility of Bryony listening.

Nurse Mitchell   Go on, say it.

Cal whispers.

Cal   Yeah, me epilepsy. You told me straight, what I had to do. You didn't make it seem like some big deal.

Nurse Mitchell   It can still be serious.

Cal   Yeah, but I can handle it.

Cal turns away to leave.

Scene 7 *(Internal): Dayroom*

Darren and James play tiddly winks. Lee sits reading 'Shoot'.

James   It's my turn to tiddle.

Darren   Go on then . . .

James flicks the counter and misses.

Darren   You missed.

James   It's a faulty wink.

Darren   I'll show you a skill tiddle.

Rowena comes in eating a giant bag of crisps. Darren and James give her a 'not you again' look and pretend to be over-engrossed in their game. Rowena pointedly ignores them.

Rowena   Hiya Lee.

Lee grunts.

Rowena   D'you want a crisp?

Lee checks for staff.

Rowena   Aren't you supposed to eat these?

Lee   I need to build meself up.

Rowena   I like crisps, don't you, Lee? In fact I like all kinds of food. In fact I can't think of any food I don't like . . . except cabbage . . . and purple jelly . . . and that yellow stuff on birthday cakes . . .

Darren and James just look at her. Lee takes a handful of crisps and then gets back to his magazine.

Rowena	Have you yeard the DJ? He sounds like a rusty gate. He had a dead sexy voice an'all. I wouldn't mind being a disc jockey . . .
Darren	You!
Rowena	They have women jockeys in the Grand National you know.
James	What – playing records?
Rowena	No, but it's the principle in't it.

Darren is bored.

Darren	Is it?

Rowena suddenly has an idea!

Rowena	I'm going to ask if I can be the disc jockey . . .
James	Go away!
Rowena	. . . let him rest his voice.
Lee	What about our ear drums?

Rowena is excited, in a world of her own.

Rowena	I'll lay some groovy sounds on you. The whole of Sparkies will be hoppin' and poppin'. I'll be rappin' and yappin'.
James	What's new?

Rowena is about to leave. She gives Lee her crisps.

Rowena	You can have these, Lee.
Lee	Ta.
Rowena	. . . I've got six more packets in my locker.

She goes out of the door, copying the DJ.

Rowena	Good morning Sparkies . . .

Dr Gallagher passes her on the way in. Lee has not seen him as he gets stuck into the crisps. Dr Gallagher motions to Darren and James to leave. They can see Dr Gallagher means business and go. Dr Gallagher goes straight for the crisps and grabs them off the unsuspecting Lee.

Lee	What d'you do that for?

Dr Gallagher	You've been told already, but I'll tell you again. Because your kidneys aren't working your body can't get rid of harmful substances.
Lee	I know all that – Sister Meadows did a test and said my potassium level was low, so I was allowed some.

Dr Gallagher looks at him.

Lee	Straight up.
Dr Gallagher	Yeah, well, I'm sorry about the crisps then. But maybe it shows how important it is that you stick to the diet. Especially when you're back home and we're not around . . .

Nurse Langdon enters and senses some tension.

Nurse Langdon	What's up?
Dr Gallagher	Caught him eating crisps . . . but he tells me his potassium level was low.
Nurse Langdon	Since when?

Lee realises he has been rumbled. Dr Gallagher is angry.

Dr Gallagher	It's no good trying to fool us here, Lee. You're the fool stuffing yourself with things that become poisons in your body.

He speaks to Nurse Langdon.

Dr Gallagher	You're supposed to keep an eye on him.
Nurse Langdon	I can't spend all my time on children's ward, I'm supposed to be on the renal unit, you know.

Dr Gallagher nods an acknowledgement of this fact.

Lee	Yeah, I'm sorry. I'm bored. When am I going home?
Dr Gallagher	When you realise you've got a serious illness and that you can live a pretty normal life if you accept responsibility for it . . .
Nurse Langdon	And all that goes with that . . .

Keely rushes in.

Keely	Dr Gallagher – can you come to the baby ward – it's little Jack.

Dr Gallagher gets up and leaves. Lee speaks to Nurse Langdon.

Lee	Sorry for getting you in bother.
Nurse Langdon	I can take care of myself. What do we have to do to make you take care of yourself?

Scene 8 *(Internal): Baby ward*

Dr Gallagher examines Baby Jack. Sister Meadows is present and Mrs Bevans looks on nervously. Keely is in the background.

Mrs Bevans	He just screamed out in agony. I couldn't do anything. Look at the colour of him.

Keely goes to comfort Mrs Bevans.

Sister Meadows	Keely, take Mrs Bevans for a cup of tea.
Mrs Bevans	I want to do something to help him.

Dr Gallagher tries to reassure Mrs Bevans.

Dr Gallagher	G'on, he'll be all right. Honest.

Sister Meadows speaks to Mrs Bevans.

Sister Meadows	We'll let you know what's happening.

Mrs Bevans begins to leave. Sister Meadows and Dr Gallagher continue examining Jack.

Sister Meadows	Blood in the stools.
Dr Gallagher	Doesn't look as if the enema's cleared the intussusception.

He straightens up.

Dr Gallagher	Theatre.

We see Mrs Bevans, who has stopped at the door on hearing this.

Scene 9 *(Internal): Ward office*

Mrs Bevans is in tears. Dr Gallagher is on the phone. Dr Woods reassures Mrs Bevans.

Mrs Bevans	I've been dreading this.
Dr Woods	As the surgeon said, the sooner he has the operation the better.
Mrs Bevans	Why does it have to be my baby . . .?
	She looks up.
Mrs Bevans	Can't you wait . . .?
	She is grasping at straws.
Mrs Bevans	He might get better. Couldn't you just leave it a while?
Dr Woods	There's always the danger of a complication if we delay.
	Dr Gallagher is still on the phone.
Dr Gallagher	Thanks. He's on his way.
	Rowena hovers impatiently around the door but sees it is not appropriate to enter. Dr Gallagher puts the phone down.
Dr Gallagher	They're ready in theatre.
Dr Woods	Mr Strickland will be operating. He couldn't be in better hands.
	Dr Gallagher collects some notes.
Mrs Bevans	Can I go with him?
Dr Gallagher	Course.
	Dr Gallagher and Mrs Bevans go to the baby ward. Dr Woods watches for a moment. She then unravels a computer print-out. Rowena appears at the door.
Rowena	Dr Woods . . .
Dr Woods	Yes, Rowena.
Rowena	You are the boss here?
	Dr Woods smiles.
Dr Woods	Sometimes I wonder.
	Dr Gallagher sticks his head round the door.
Dr Gallagher	If you see Lee Jones, just gee him up about sticking to his diet.

Dr Woods nods.

Dr Woods   Anything rather than this.

Indicates the print-out. Dr Gallagher goes.

Rowena   I knew Lee shouldn't eat those crisps . . . anyway, you're probably important enough to answer my question.

Dr Woods   Well, your operation was very successful, and if there are no complications you should soon be home. It's not causing you any problems is it?

Rowena   Oh no, that's all right.

Dr Woods   Good. What's so important then?

Rowena   The DJ's losing his voice. He's playing records nearly all the time. He isn't rapping.

Dr Woods   Occupational hazard.

Rowena   Well, I'm willing to stand in – I'm really good at talking a lot.

Dr Woods   I could certainly vouch for you on that score.

Rowena   Could you swing it?

Dr Woods   I don't really have any say over the hospital radio . . .

Rowena is downcast.

Dr Woods   . . . but I'll see what I can do.

Rowena is chuffed.

Rowena   They should make you boss of the whole hospital. I knew you would. You're an inspiration to women. I might be a doctor one day and it will all be thanks to you.

We see Dr Woods who is also chuffed!

Scene 10*(Internal): Sluice room*

Nurse Grahams finishes washing her hair. She towels it. Nurse Mags watches amused.

Nurse Mags   Good – can I have my sink back now. I bet you've clogged it with hair.

Nurse Grahams looks in the mirror.

Nurse Grahams Boring, boring, boring. I hate looking boring.

Nurse Mags You'll never be boring, Nurse Grahams.

Nurse Grahams I look boring though . . .

She muses.

Nurse Grahams Just how my parents liked me – plain, dull . . .

Nurse Mags It might sound daft but my old feller was the same.

Nurse Grahams looks. Nurse Mags smiles.

Nurse Mags I was young once you know.

Nurse Grahams Me first proper boyfriend was the same – wanted me to be plain Jane. Didn't even want me to have a career.

Nurse Mags So you upped sticks and left it all behind.

Nurse Grahams Yeah and look at me – people are still telling me how I should look. Just 'coz I dress up it doesn't mean I'm a dawk.

Nurse Mags I don't know what a 'dawk' is – but I reckon you'll make a good nurse, even if you do dress up like a Christmas tree . . . But for now, put these on.

She throws her a packet of tights. Nurse Grahams reads the packet.

Nurse Grahams American Tan – my granny wears these.

Nurse Mags Oy, that'll do – they're mine.

Nurse Grahams Yeah, I knew really.

Nurse Mags gives a playful dig.

Nurse Mags It's all right. When you're a nursing officer in ten years you might thank me for those.

Nurse Grahams kisses Mags.

Nurse Grahams You're a darling . . .

Scene 11 *(Internal): Hydrotherapy pool*

The physio is in the pool with Bryony. She is moving quite freely, unaided in the water.

Physio You'll be doing the Channel swim at this rate.

Bryony I wish it was half as easy to move on dry land.

Physio Don't worry, that will come.

Bryony They keep saying it will burn out, then just when I think I'm getting better if flares up again.

Physio The thing is to keep working at it so when you do get a remission you're in good shape.

Bryony This is better than lying in bed all day.

Physio notices a new arrival. Bryony follows her gaze. Cal is at the entrance, watching.

Bryony The water's lovely.

Cal I came to throw you some fish.

He imitates a sea lion. Bryony attempts to splash him but cannot summon the strength.

Bryony Good job I can't splash you.

The physio is amused by this.

Physio I can.

She swings her arm and splashes Cal.

Physio You should have brought your trunks.

She moves off to see someone else.

Bryony It's great in here.

She swims to the side of the pool and Cal crouches by her.

Cal It was brilliant last summer, when it was dead hot. Me and me mates used to go swimming in this old quarry near us.

Bryony I didn't think you had any . . .

Cal What?

Bryony Mates.

Cal I've got loads.

Bryony	I've never seen them visit you.
	Cal is defensive.
Cal	Course they don't.
Bryony	Don't they know you're in hospital?
	(*Cal lies.*)
Cal	I've told 'em not to bother that's all . . . it's a long way for 'em to come.
	Cal stands, turns and goes. Bryony wants to follow him but cannot. Bryony speaks quietly.
Bryony	See you later, Cal.

Scene 12 (*Internal*): *Children's ward*

Dr Woods, with Rowena, meets Nurse Grahams who has finished doing Lucy's dressings. Lucy goes off to the dayroom.

Rowena	Urrgh. I hate your tights.
Dr Woods	Rowena – that's not the way to get someone to do you a favour.
Nurse Grahams	It's all right – I'm developing a rhino's hide.
Rowena	That's what them tights look like.
Dr Woods	Rowena wants to put her vocal abilities to better use.
Rowena	What?
Dr Woods	Do you think you could take her up to the radio station to see if she could do a bit of DJ-ing?
Nurse Grahams	Yes, sure.
	Rowena brightens up. Darren and James are horror-struck. Dr Woods walks back to the office. Rowena speaks to Nurse Grahams.
Rowena	Your legs aren't that horrible really.
Nurse Grahams	Come on then.

Scene 13*(Internal): Children's ward*

Jack hurries with his trolley after Dr Woods. He catches up, nearly mowing her down.

Jack   Dr Woods . . .

Dr Woods   Hello Jack.

Jack   I know it's not strictly pack-drill . . .

Dr Woods is puzzled.

Jack   . . . but I wonder if you wouldn't mind, as you might say, divulging the condition of one of the patients.

Dr Woods   Who do you want to know about?

Jack   Jack.

Dr Woods   Jack?

Jack   Yes, Baby Jack. I saw them wheeling him off.

Dr Woods   He's having an operation to remove a blockage.

Jack   Will he pull through?

Dr Woods   We certainly hope so.

Jack   Poor mite.

Dr Woods touches Jack's arm.

Dr Woods   I'm sure he'll be all right.

Dr Woods moves off. Jack is deep in thought. He collects himself.

Jack   Thanks Doctor . . . thanks . . .

He wheels the trolley slowly on, past Darren and James at the table.

James   This is serious – How can they let her go on the radio?

Darren   We'll have to stop it happening, that's all there is to it.

James   Maybe we could get the doctors to take her tonsils out.

Darren   They've done that already.

James   We could blow up the radio station.

Darren pulls a face at that non-starter.

James   How we going to stop her, then?

Darren   By using our brains.

A long empty silence follows.

Scene 14 *(Internal): Maternity/ultrasound scan*

We see Keely in a smock on the couch, a scanner on her stomach. A radiologist and a nurse from out-patients are present. The radiologist points to the screen.

Radiologist   There you can see the heart beating. That's the head. There's the spine. You might be just able to make out the arms and legs.

Keely   I think so . . . Is everything all right?

Radiologist   We'll make a report for the consultant.

Keely   Yes . . . Course . . .

She hesitates.

Keely   But as far as you can see, is everything all right?

The radiologist smiles.

Radiologist   I can't see anything to worry about.

Keely relaxes.

Scene 15 *(Internal): Boiler room*

Darren and James bring a reluctant Lee in.

Lee   This better be worth it.

James   It's a matter of life and death.

Darren   How can we stop that Rowena giving us earache on the radio?

Lee   Don't listen.

James   They'll have it blasting out of their ear phones.

Darren   Yeah, and if she is on radio, she'll think she's a super star – she'll have something else to rabbit on about.

Lee	Cut her off then.
Darren and James	Eh, yeah . . .
	A blank pause follows.
Darren and **James**	How?
Lee	They must have a master switch somewhere on the ward.
Darren	Where?
Lee	I don't know . . . trace the wire from the headsets.
Darren and James	Eh, yeah.

Scene 16 *(Internal): Operating theatre/waiting area*

Mrs Bevans paces about. Dr Gallagher sits.

Mrs Bevans	Why's it taking so long? You said it was simple. I knew I shouldn't have agreed to the operation. If anything happens it will be my fault.
	Dr Gallagher firm but gentle.
Dr Gallagher	Look, we tried an alternative treatment first. That didn't do the trick and so he's having surgery. There was no other option – and don't forget the vast majority of operations are successful – that's why we do them.
Mrs Bevans	But I don't care about a million other operations. I just want this one to work.
Dr Gallagher	Yeah, I know.
	Mrs Bevans sits, a little calmer.

Scene 17 *(Internal): Baby ward*

We see Baby Jack's empty cot. Jack Crossley enters. He looks at the cot then takes a small cuddly novelty toy from his pocket and hangs it up in view of the cot. Jack speaks to the toy.

Jack   Keep an eye on him, little feller.

He then feels rather foolish, collects himself and leaves.

Scene 18 *(Internal): Maternity/waiting area*

Keely   Fine, thanks.

Billy   Don't go into detail, will you. How's the baby?

Keely   Fine.

Billy   Keely, let me in will you, it's my kid an'all.

Keely   Yeah, I know, sorry.

Billy   What did they say about it?

Keely   They send a report to the consultant . . .

She continues more reassuringly.

Keely   . . . but from what they said everything seems all right.

Billy   Great.

Keely   Just one thing . . .

Billy is concerned.

Billy   What's up?

Keely   Well, the baby's pretty big.

Billy   There's nowt wrong with that.

Keely   No – it means I'm further gone than I thought. They reckon it might be due just when I'm taking my exams.

Billy   Oh, we're back to exams are we – That old . . .

Keely   Billy. They matter to me. I want to stand on my own two feet, remember?

Billy's hurt by this. Keely relents. She remembers the photo she is holding.

Keely   Here, look.

Billy   What is it?

Keely   It's the scan.

Billy is moved.

Billy   Brilliant.

Keely points at the photo.

Keely   There's the head, the spine. Honest you should
see it on the screen – its brilliant – you can see
its little heartbeat, everything.

*They both look at the photo – a moment of shared
intimacy.*

Scene 19 *(Internal): Hospital radio studio*

*A record plays as the DJ is gargling with TCP.
There are throat lozenges on his console. Nurse
Grahams taps on the door and enters with
Rowena, who is awe-struck. Nurse Grahams
whispers.*

Nurse Grahams   I hope we're not interrupting.

The DJ croaks.

DJ   No . . . I think we might have to go off the air.
Play sombre music like it's a national disaster –
my voice has gone.

Nurse Grahams braces herself.

Nurse Grahams   Well . . . Rowena here wonders if she could help
you out, stand in for you.

DJ   Well, she can't sound worse than me.

He moves his chair, and pats another seat.

DJ   Take the hot-seat, Rowena . . . I'll wise you up.

*Rowena, almost in a trance, sits. Rowena is about
to start her new career as a radio presenter. The
DJ sits by as a record finishes, Nurse Grahams
looks on. The DJ croaks:*

DJ   Now here is Rowena Easson. Sparkies answer to
Liz Kershaw . . . A Joan of Arc of the airwaves
sitting in for someone whose soothing tones will
ease the troubled brow – and give my clack a
rest.

Rowena's eyes are glazed with fear.

Scene 20 *(Internal): Children's ward/Radio studio*

This scene switches between action in the radio studio and action on the ward.

Youngers, including Lee, Cal, Bryony, Lucy (with her dummy in her mouth) and Danny, listen to the radio. James and Darren, a little apart, study an earphone socket.

In radio studio. Rowena is nervous.

Rowena Good afternoon . . . I mean morning . . . Sparkies.

She whispers.

Rowena What do I say now?

On ward.

Darren Blimey, she's lost for words.

James They should let her be DJ all the time if it keeps her quiet.

Kids in paroxyms of laughter.

In radio studio.

Rowena Oh, yes, play a record.

A horrible scratching is heard and a record goes on. Nurse Grahams and the DJ cannot bear to listen to Rowena. A record plays. The DJ and Nurse Grahams try to encourage Rowena.

Rowena What do I talk about?

Nurse Grahams You know what DJ's talk about – any old rubbish.

She turns apologetically to the DJ.

Nurse Grahams Well some do.

DJ Just say anything that comes into your head.

Rowena thinks.

Rowena It's empty.

The DJ is almost despairing but the record ends and he's forced to act.

DJ Go for it.

Rowena goes on automatic pilot.

Rowena   Hi – my name's Rowena. I like dancing and eating. I've just had my tonsils done but all you listeners out there will be pleased to know I'm eating again, and my voice is in very very good shape . . .

Scene 21 *(Internal): Children's ward*

James and Darren are near the office. We see the speaker-ducting which is now up by the ceiling.

Darren   It's dead easy this, look it goes up there.

He points.

James   Say the staff find out.

Darren   They should give us a medal.

James   They'll do their fruit.

Darren   What's worse – Rowena rabbiting, or a bit of talking to off the staff.

James considers.

James   You're right . . .

Scene 22 *(Internal): Hydrotherapy pool*

Physio   Come on, concentrate.

Bryony   Don't, I'm trying to listen to this. It's really funny.

Physio   Do you want a walk?

Bryony   No. Go on, you should hear this.

Physio   Why, what is it?

Bryony   It's Rowena, trying to be a DJ.

Physio   What?

Bryony   It's Rowena trying to be a DJ. It's really funny. Just wait a minute.

Physio   What's she doing?

Bryony   She's making a fool of herself. Do you want a listen?

Physio   Go on.

Scene 23 *(Internal): Children's ward*

James	Right, get me a chair – I can't see where it goes to.

James, game for anything, climbs on Darren's shoulders who nearly collapses. Nurse Mags and Nurse Mitchell wheel on the food trolley. James sees the staff arrive.

James	On no . . .
Nurse Mitchell	What are you doing?
James	Er . . . training for the circus.
Nurse Mitchell	Well, get down before you fall down.

James gets down.

Scene 24 *(Internal): Radio studio*

Rowena has a record on turntable.

Rowena	And now here's a special song for the staff.

She speaks to herself.

Rowena	Now what's it called . . . oh dear. Well, it's on now, so nothing personal . . . It's called 'Shut Up yer Face'.

Record plays.

Scene 25 *(Internal): Children's ward.*

Darren whispers.

Darren	I'll tell you what – you be a decoy.
James	A what?
Darren	Go and do something to occupy the staff.
James	Right.

He pauses.

James	Like what?
Darren	Use your intelligence . . .

James is blank.

Darren	Do anything – juggle if you like.

James   I can't juggle. Anyway I don't think they believed what I said about the circus.

Scene 26 *(Internal): Radio studio/Children's ward*

This scene switches between action in radio studio and action on ward.

Rowena   But before I do, I'd like to say a few words to the staff, because our staff are very, very special, very very dedicated.

On ward.

The children are listening to Rowena's performance.

Cal   She always was a creep.

In studio.

Rowena   And not just for you patient-types. For the dedicated staff too – especially the best doctor in the whole world – Dr Woods. The woman who saw my talent.

Scene 27 *(Internal): Outside ward office*

Darren   Look, the wire leads into the office.

He pushes James towards a trolley.

Darren   Now you go and divert them.

James reluctantly heads for the food trolley, still not sure what he is going to do. Darren slips into the office. James gets to Nurse Mitchell and Nurse Mags and decides to go for it.

James   What's going on here? I'm supposed to be a sick person on a special diet, but what do I get? I'll tell you what I get – the bread is like cardboard, the soup's like glue, and the water's like soup.

Nurse Mitchell and Nurse Mags are sufficiently gobsmacked by this performance not to notice Darren in the office. The record finishes.

Scene 28 *(Internal): Radio studio*

The DJ and Nurse Grahams are bored. Rowena rattles on.

Rowena   I bet all you listeners out there are having a ball – I know I am.

Nurse Grahams and the DJ just look at each other.

Scene 29 *(Internal): Children's ward*

James is at the trolley. Nurse Mags and Nurse Mitchell are bemused by his performance.

Nurse Mitchell   And what was all that about?

Nurse Mags   You've never complained about the food before.

James, embarrassed, looks towards the office for inspiration. Darren gives him a thumbs up.

James   Oh, no, the food's very nice. What's for dinner, I can't wait . . .

Scene 30 *(Internal): Office*

We see Darren's finger on a switch labelled 'PA'. He presses it.

Scene 31 *(Internal): Children's ward*

As before only with Rowena booming over the PA. Kids all laughing. We see the speaker. Darren comes from the office.

Rowena   (voice only): . . . Dr Gallagher is nice, but scruffy. And as I know Nurse Mitchell will be too busy to be listening to the radio, I can tell you she's nice but grumpy with it . . .

Darren and James go to sneak off.

Nurse Mitchell is on her way to the office. She sees Darren and James

Nurse Mitchell   What have you two been up to?

Darren is sheepish

Darren	I pressed the wrong switch!
Nurse Mitchell	You most certainly did.

Nurse Mags can scarcely contain herself. We see the kids in the ward laughing. Nurse Mitchell goes into the office and switches off the PA.

Scene 32 *(Internal): Radio studio*

Rowena I've never had such a wonderful time, I'm enjoying this so much I don't think I'll ever be able to stop talking. I can go on and on and on and on and on . . .

Scene 33 *(External): Hospital grounds*

Lee walks with his mate Ben. They both kick leaves, twigs, or whatever.

Ben I'll tell you Lee, we've got no chance in the semis without you. Dick Rogers 'as got two left feet and I think he keeps his brain in one of 'em.

Lee laughs.

Lee It's this Sat'day.

Ben I thought you might be out before then.

Lee So did I.

Ben You won't be able to play any road.

Lee Why not?

Ben Well, you wouldn't be in here would you if you were fit.

Lee I'm no invalid . . .

Ben I didn't mean . . .

Lee All I have to do is watch what I eat and have me blood washed out. I can't see how that's gonna stop me playing. Look at Brian Robbo.

Ben Captain Marvel.

Lee jumps and does a header then raises a fist as if he's scored.

Scene 34 *(Internal): Baby ward*

Baby Jack is back from the recovery room. He is sleeping. Sister Meadows checks his temperature, as Mrs Bevans and Dr Gallagher look on.

Dr Gallagher   That's OK and the surgeon was pleased.

Mrs Bevans   Thank God.

Dr Gallagher   He'll probably sleep through now.

Mrs Bevans   I'll sit with him.

Mrs Bevans sits near the cot. Sister Meadows leaves.

Sister Meadows   Call us if you want anything. I'll pop in again a bit later.

Mrs Bevans   Sister Meadows – d'you know who left that?

She nods towards the toy Jack Crossley left.

Sister Meadows   I've a good idea.

Mrs Bevans looks.

Sister Meadows   Mr Crossley – he's been like a cat on hot bricks since he heard young Jack was having an operation.

Sister Meadows smiles and leaves. Dr Gallagher is about to follow her.

Mrs Bevans   Dr Gallagher . . .

Dr Gallagher   Don't thank me – it's Mr Strickland the surgeon . . .

Mrs Bevans   No, I'm grateful to everyone for what you've done for Jack . . .

Dr Gallagher touches her shoulder.

Dr Gallagher   You have a bit of a rest.

Mrs Bevans   . . . but I want to thank you. I don't think I could have got through the day without you.

Dr Gallagher   All part of the service.

Episode Six
by John Chambers

Scene 1 *(Internal): Children's ward*

Lee is removing his poster of Brian Robson.

James   Can I have that?

We see Lee is preparing to leave. His bag is on the bed.

Lee   I thought you supported one of them Scouse teams.

James   I support England too.

Lee gives James the poster and continues packing. Darren approaches.

Darren   Ey, James, come here.

James puts the poster on his bed. He exits with Darren. Cal speaks to Lee.

Cal   You lucky dog.

Lee   I'll be back in for dialysis, so you haven't seen the back of me.

Bryony   You make sure you look after yourself.

Lee continues packing. Bryony speaks to Cal.

Bryony   I can't see myself ever getting out of this bed. Sometimes I feel better, then the next day it's . .

Cal   Course you'll get out. Still it won't be anything to do with the staff here – I think they guess what's up with us half the time.

They are interrupted by the giggling of James and Darren who are smuggling a wheelchair out of the ward.

Cal   Oy, what you two doing?

James   Goin' on the 'wheelie run'.

Bryony   What's that?

Darren   See how fast we can go round all the corridors

and get back 'ere.

James speaks to Darren.

James Have you got your watch on?

Darren Yeah.

Darren sits down in the wheelchair.

James What you doin'?

Darren What's it look like?

James I'm driving.

He thinks.

James Is driving sitting in or pushing?

Darren thinks.

Darren I don't know.

James I'm in first.

Darren I am.

James I wanted to be Nigel Mansell.

Darren You can be his Honda engine.

James makes a revving sound. Darren checks his watch.

Darren 5–4–3–2–1– they're off.

James pushes the chair through the doors. Lee is moving off up ward. There are adlib 'goodbyes'.

Rowena Will you miss us?

Lee Yeah, I'll think I've gone deaf – not hearing you parroting on all the time.

Rowena You what . . .

Lee Hey, we might be at Wembley together yet – you doing the cheerleading.

Cal chimes in.

Cal She might be doing the radio commentary.

Rowena is serious.

Rowena I've given up my radio career.

Nurse Langdon comes along.

Nurse Langdon Hi Rowena! Still here, Lee?

Lee	Just waiting for me mam to pick me up.
Nurse Langdon	Come on then . . .
	Nurse Langdon and Lee go towards the office, Lee saying 'see you', etc. to the other kids.
Nurse Langdon	Now remember . . .
Lee	Yeah I know.
	He recites, good-naturedly.
Lee	Keep to the diet . . . Look after my fistula.
	He indicates his arm
Lee	. . . Keep my dialysis appointments . . .
Nurse Langdon	. . . And no football.
Lee	Bye Lucy. I was just coming to that.
Nurse Langdon	I hope so.
Lee	Thanks. I was brickin' it when I first went on dialysis – you were all right.
Nurse Langdon	You've done well.
	He puts on a footballer voice.
Nurse Langdon	The boy done good, Brian – 'e must be over the moon.
Lee	I am over the moon to be on me way.
	Nurse Langdon pats his shoulder.
Nurse Langdon	Yeah, well, take care.

Scene 2 *(Internal): Baby ward*

Dr Woods examines Baby Jack. Sister Meadows is present along with Mrs Bevans.

Dr Woods	He's doing really well.
	She speaks to Sister Meadows
Dr Woods	We'll keep him on fluids a while longer.
Mrs Bevans	No more operations?
Dr Woods	No.
	She smiles.

Dr Woods	Well, not for that anyway.
Mrs Bevans	I don't think I could take any more.
Dr Woods	How are you feeling? We sometimes concentrate so much on the patients, we forget about the parents.
Mrs Bevans	I still can't believe he's all right, but I'm OK – everyone's been so good – Dr Gallagher . . ., Sister, everyone . . .
Dr Woods	Good.

Dr Woods leaves and Sister Meadows is about to follow.

Mrs Bevans	Oh, Sister.

Sister Meadows waits.

Mrs Bevans	Hannah will be staying with me tomorrow, if that's OK?
Sister Meadows	Sure. Does her dad never have her?
Mrs Bevans	He never offers, and she wouldn't go if he did.
Sister Meadows	I think it's a good idea for youngsters to get to know the children's ward – then if they ever do have to come in, it's not the terrible place they imagine.
Mrs Bevans	No, it's great. Dead friendly, relaxed, isn't it?
Sister Meadows	Sometimes it gets a bit fraught.

Sister Meadows leaves.

Scene 3 *(Internal): Long corridor*

Darren and James are on the 'wheelie run'. James is pushing. James commentates.

James	Oh yes, and they're breaking all records – quite remarkable. But the engine's going to blow up if it doesn't have a rest.
Darren	Ah, you can't stop now. Come on, faster. Burn it. Step on the gas.
James	We need a refill.

They swing round a corner, making braking screeches, only to see Nurse Mitchell backing out of a side room with a trolley. They do a quick u-turn and disappear. Nurse Mitchell turns, having heard something – but it must be her imagination. James and Darren have raced round another corner. James gets in the chair.

James Aren't we disqualified?

Darren Na – pit stop.

He speaks through a cupped hand megaphone.

Darren 5–4–3–2–1 – and they're off.

He pushes like mad as they speed off.

Scene 4 *(Internal): Children's ward*

Nurse Mags and Nurse Grahams chat as they push a laundry trolley, unaware that Rowena, in a world of her own, is practising dance steps, a few steps behind them.

Nurse Mags He's a good-looking feller, that Nurse Langdon off Renal.

Rowena is interested.

Nurse Grahams Do you think so?

Nurse Mags nods.

Nurse Grahams I hadn't noticed.

Nurse Mags pulls a disbelieving face. Nurse Grahams is wry.

Nurse Grahams Anyway Mags – he's too young for you.

Nurse Mags I'm sure that this place is haunted . . .

Rowena is really interested. Nurse Mags continues.

Nurse Mags . . . the amount of pillow cases that go missing.

Nurse Grahams The Ghost of South Park . . . He's coming to get you Nurse Mags.

Rowena, wide-eyed, just has to tell someone. She leaves. Nurse Grahams sticks a sheet over her head and makes ghost noises.

Nurse Mags   You big daft pudding. Hallowe'en's been and gone.

Nurse Grahams removes the sheet.

Nurse Grahams   You've got to admit it Nurse Mags. It's more fun than bed-making and laundry.

Nurse Mags   Oh aye, but this has still to be done at the end of it all.

Nurse Grahams is mock serious.

Nurse Grahams   Yes, Nurse Mags, right, Nurse Mags.

They take the trolley towards the sluice room.

Nurse Grahams   Can I ask a nursing question, Nurse Mags?

Nurse Mags   Go on.

Nurse Grahams   Do you think Florence Nightingale ever dressed up as a ghost?

Nurse Mags   Not unless she was as daft as you.

Nurse Grahams laughs.

James   Beep, beep, mind your backs!

James is now being pushed by Darren around the corner. They slide to a halt. Nurse Mags and Nurse Grahams are taken aback.

Darren   I was just giving him some exercise.

James mutters.

James   You're having the exercise.

Darren   Oh yeah – I'm having the exercise.

Nurse Mags   Take that chair back to the ward – we don't want you or anyone else getting hurt. And walk – both of you.

James gets out of the chair. They slowly push it back and disappear round corner. Nurse Mags and Nurse Grahams push laundry into children's intensive care. Darren and James' heads peep round the corner to make sure the coast is clear.

Scene 5 *(Internal): Children's ward*

Lucy is in bed with the customary dummy in her mouth. Rowena is excited, telling her the news.

Rowena It's official.

Lucy What?

Rowena The Ghost of South Park.

Lucy What?

Rowena The hospital's haunted.

Lucy What? Ghosts and ghoulies?

Rowena And spooks.

Lucy How do you know?

Rowena looks smug.

Rowena Nurse Grahams and Nurse Mags told me.

Lucy takes a precautionary look about.

Lucy Don't be daft!

Scene 6 *(Internal): Children's ward*

Cal is helping Bryony adjust her position in bed. For the first time he is aware of how the slightest movement can hurt her.

Cal Is that any better?

Bryony A bit . . . Trouble is I have to rest, but lying in bed gives me bed sores.

Cal Can't they do owt for it?

Bryony Going to the pool's best – it still hurts, but it's kind of soothing – and it's not as boring as just lying still.

Cal Are you all right?

Again she tries to adjust her position and gets a real jab of pain. Her discomfort is matched by the frustration on Cal's face at not being able to help her.

Scene 7 *(Internal): Ward office*

Sister Meadows, followed by Nurse Mitchell, enters office.

Sister Meadows	. . . It's about Cal Spicer . . .
Nurse Mitchell	Oh . . .
Sister Meadows	. . . The way you've been treating him . . .

Nurse Mitchell jumps to wrong conclusions.

Nurse Mitchell	If you've got cause for complaint . . .
Sister Meadows	Just the opposite.

Nurse Mitchell just looks at her.

Sister Meadows I just wanted to say you've been smashing, the way you've got through to him. He's not the easiest lad.

Nurse Mitchell is wry.

Nurse Mitchell He seems to respond to my . . . straightforward approach.

Sister Meadows I think you're really helping him to come to terms with his problems.

Nurse Mitchell Just doing my job.

Sister Meadows is firm.

Sister Meadows You've given him more than that – well done.

Cal enters, angry.

Cal	I might have known it.
Nurse Mitchell	Don't just barge in here.

Cal is in full flow.

Cal There's people out there who need help and you're sittin' round talkin' about your horoscopes or something.

Scene 8 *(Internal): Children's ward*

Cal follows Sister Meadows and Nurse Mitchell back to Bryony's bed. Bryony is bemused by the sudden attention. Sister Meadows and Nurse

	Mitchell are both sides of the bed ready to give Bryony, a physical examination.
Sister Meadows	Is the pain worse, Bryony?
Bryony	It's the same as usual . . . What's the matter?
Nurse Mitchell	Cal was worried.
	Bryony looks at Cal, as do Sister Meadows and Nurse Mitchell. Cal is embarrassed.
Cal	Yeah, well, you should do something for her.
Sister Meadows	We're trying.
Nurse Mitchell	It's good you're concerned about other patients, Cal.
	Cal is defensive.
Cal	Yeah, well, someone's got to be haven't they?
Sister Meadows	You'll feel better after hydrotherapy – the porter will be up to take you soon.
Bryony	Oh great.
Cal	I'll take her.
	Nurse Mitchell and Sister Meadows are both surprised.
Bryony	Can he take me?
	Sister Meadows is unsure.
Sister Meadows	The porter will do it.
Cal	What d'you think I'm going to do – let her roll downstairs or drop her down the lift shaft.
Nurse Mitchell	Just calm down, Cal. Don't go off at the deep end.
Sister Meadows	If you want to be given responsibility just learn to talk things through.
Bryony	Could Cal take me down?
	Sister Meadows looks briefly at Nurse Mitchell who shows her approval.
Sister Meadows	All right – but remember this is a hospital . . .
Cal	Yeah, yeah, yeah . . .
Bryony	We will.

Sister Meadows	I mean it Cal – you're both responsible for each other.
Bryony	Thanks Sister Meadows.
	Sister Meadows leaves for the office.
Nurse Mitchell	I hope you heard all that Cal?
Cal	Course . . . Pity they won't let me have a dip in that pool.
	Nurse Mitchell shakes her head and smiles.

Scene 9 *(Internal): Main corridor*

Lee, with bags, and Mrs Jones are waiting for the lift as they leave.

Mrs Jones	That blimmin' solicitor – all I had to do was sign the form for the affidavit for the divorce, and I was waiting for over an hour. I bet he sticks it on his bill, for wear and tear on his seat.
Lee	Is it settled then?
	Lift arrives. Mrs Jones puts her arm round Lee as they enter.
Mrs Jones	Be absolute in a couple of weeks.
Lee	Good riddance to him. Maybe he'll stop interfering. Get the message, stay out of our lives.
Mrs Jones	Ey, come on, never mind that. You're coming home, that's the main thing.
	Nurse Grahams runs up.
Nurse Grahams	I thought I'd missed you. I just wanted to say 'goodbye'.
Lee	Yeah, I'll see you, Nurse Grahams.
Nurse Grahams	Take care and . . .
Lee	I know . . .
Mrs Jones	Don't worry – he will.
	Doors close. Nurse Grahams heads off to the ward.

Scene 10 *(Internal): Children's ward*

The doors of the side corridor bang open as James pushes Darren in, out of breath and coughing. Both are exhausted, obviously they have overdone it. Nurse Grahams, returning from the lift, sees this.

Nurse Grahams   Come on, you two, that's enough of that. You were told before.

Cal speaks to Darren:

Cal   What happened to Nigel Mansell – did his engine blow up?

Nurse Grahams   Darren, have a rest.

Darren gets out of the wheelchair and unprotestingly goes to his bed and flops.

James   I think I need some sugar. I feel shaky.

Nurse Grahams   You go and lie down for a bit and I'll test your blood sugar. Be back in a minute.

James   Aw, no – I don't have to wee in another bottle do I?

Nurse Grahams   It's a blood test.

James pulls a face, but is quite glad to get on to his bed. Cal gets the wheelchair.

Cal   You should have him seen to by a vet.

Cal speaks to Bryony.

Cal   Right Madam, your chauffeur's here.

He helps Bryony get slowly into the chair.

Cal   Ey, Tom and Jerry . . .

James and Darren look.

Cal   What time did you do the 'wheelie run' in?

Darren still breathless.

Darren   Twenty one minutes, forty-three seconds.

Cal   Pathetic

James   We had pit stops.

Cal   We'll do it in under fifteen.

Bryony	What?
Cal	You an' me.
Bryony	We can't . . .
Darren	Chicken.

He clucks like a chicken. Bryony finally gets into the chair.

Bryony	We'll see about that.
Cal	Are you sure you'll be all right?
Darren	Are you bottlin' it now, Spicer?
Bryony	We'll show you. Ready, steady . . .

They are interrupted by the arrival of Dr Woods coming down the ward to see Darren. Dr Woods sees Bryony, Cal and the chair.

Bryony	Cal's taking me down to hydrotherapy.

Cal is surprised and impressed by Bryony's nerve. Cal is as blunt as ever.

Cal	Sister Meadows said it was OK.
Dr Woods	Fine.
Cal	Oh right . . . we'll get going then.

He pushes the chair towards the doors extremely slowly.

Dr Woods	No sudden jolts or bumps.
Cal	Right.

Bryony taps her wrist as a subtle gesture to Darren who starts his watch – just before Dr Woods arrives at his bed to listen to his chest. Bryony and Cal go through doors. Cal is not pushing as fast as we might expect.

Cal	Mebbe we better just take you to the pool.

Bryony smiles.

Bryony	Bottling out, Spicer?
Cal	You're a right one you – and I thought you were a goody-goody.
Bryony	Less gassing and just step on the gas.

Cal checks his watch.

Cal   You asked for it.

The speed with which Cal pushes takes Bryony's breath away. Cal pushes a giggling Bryony along. Bryony suddenly winces with pain.

Cal   Here we go, here we go, here we go. Is this the right way?

Bryony   Yeah, left.

Just as Cal and Bryony get to the end of the corridor they nearly collide with Bryony's parents, Mr and Mrs Shaeffer, coming through the doors. Cal screeches to a halt. We follow Bryony's gaze up the two visitors' legs . . . Bryony goes pale.

Bryony   Hello Mum . . . hello Dad . . .

They aren't pleased.

Scene 11 *(Internal): Ward office*

Dr Woods and Sister Meadows are harangued by Bryony's parents.

Mr Shaeffer   . . . Even before Bryony was admitted we were seriously considering sending her for private treatment.

Dr Woods   That's your choice.

Mrs Shaeffer   Couldn't she have a room to herself?

Dr Woods   We feel it is often better if the youngsters can be with other children – they're less isolated, less likely to brood – it's generally more beneficial.

Mr Shaeffer   But this lad is, well a delinquent. How can it be beneficial to Bryony to be in the next bed.

Sister Meadows   Cal might be a bit . . . rough and ready . . .

Mr Shaeffer   Yes . . .

Sister Meadows   But he's not a delinquent. Bryony seems to be getting on well with him – he actually cheers her up.

Mr Shaeffer	But she's ill, that's why she's in here. Goodness knows what would have happened if she'd fallen out of the chair.
Dr Woods	Yes that was quite wrong, and very dangerous. They were warned and it won't happen in the future.
Sister Meadows	That's right.
Mrs Shaeffer	The thing is, Bryony's impressionable – I suppose she's lead a fairly sheltered life.
Dr Woods	I think things might look worse to you than they actually are. The fact is she has a chronic illness which is going to need long-term treatment – surely if a relationship makes her feel positive, we mustn't just write it off.

Mr Shaeffer stands up.

Mr Shaeffer	Well, we've told her that we don't approve. And I hope you will respect our wishes by discouraging that relationship. These great democratic ideas are all very well until it's your own child that's involved.

Dr Woods is reassuring.

Dr Woods	I assure you there'll be no more speed trials in wheelchairs.

Mr Shaeffer goes to leave. Mrs Shaeffer follows – she gives a weak embarrassed smile and hesitates.

Mrs Shaeffer	We do appreciate what you're doing for Bryony.

They leave.

Sister Meadows	Talk about 'us and them'!

Dr Woods nods.

Dr Woods	Still, we'll have to have a word with Cal Spicer – Bryony's progress could have been put back weeks, months, if she'd fallen out of the chair.

Sister Meadows nods.

Sister Meadows	I'll read the riot act to both of them.

Scene 12 *(External)*: *Jones' house.*

We see the house, from a distance. The lights are on in the living room and the curtains are drawn. There is a feeling of cosiness.

Scene 13 *(Internal)*: *Jones family living room.*

Lee and Mrs Jones watch televison.

Mrs Jones	D'you ever miss him?
Lee	Who?
Mrs Jones	Your dad – and Marcus.
Lee	Why should I?
Mrs Jones	You and Marcus used to be close, good mates, – not the usual squabbling brothers.
Lee	Oh aye, some 'mate'. We didn't see him for dust when me dad went off with his fancy woman . . . I couldn't care less about either of them. They're not bothered about us. The sooner that divorce goes through the better.
Mrs Jones	Yeah . . . When you were in hospital, for the first time in my life, I felt lonely.
Lee	Well, I'm back now, so you don't have to give them the time of day. I'm going to show 'em, the pair of them. I'm going to do something with my life. I'll see you're all right an' all.
Mrs Jones	Don't do anything out of bitterness, Lee, no matter what you make out of your life. Your dad and me made that mistake.
Lee	I'm not bitter, I don't care about them that's all.

Scene 14 *(Internal)*: *Lee Jones' bedroom*

Lee looks at photos of some of his football heroes on the wall and then at photos of himself in football kit, also perhaps a medal or two he has won, and some clippings from a local paper. He takes a picture of Brian Robson. Lee speaks to himself.

Lee Nowt's goin' to get in my way. Nothing and nobody.

Scene 15 *(External): Hospital*

We see the hospital from a distance. It is windy.

Scene 16 *(Internal): Children's ward*

Rowena is awake but in bed. Her eyes watch the shadows, a flapping curtain. A radiator groans, a flapper door rattles. The following is whispered.

Rowena Lucy.

We see Lucy is still awake.

Lucy Yes.

Rowena Are you asleep?

Lucy No.

Rowena Good.

Lucy D'you think the ghost will come tonight?

Rowena If he lives here, he's bound to.

James Ey, you two, shurrup.

Rowena Do you know anything about ghosts?

James Course, I've seen *Ghostbusters II* sixteen times.

Lucy Are you frightened of them?

James Course not.

Rowena The Ghost of South Park lives in the boiler room.

James Who said?

Rowena Nurse Mags told me.

James Ey, Darren.

Darren Shurrup.

James There's a ghost in the boiler room.

Darren Who said?

Rowena Nurse Mags.

Darren sits up.

Darren	Let's go and bust it then.
Rowena	How?
James	You're dim, you.
Danny	Can I come?
Darren	As long as you don't throw a wobbler.
Rowena	Course you can come.

Scene 17 *(Internal): Boiler room corridor*

The corridor is deserted, and silent. We hear Darren quietly singing the 'Ghostbusters' tune. Then James, Rowena, Lucy and Danny shout the 'Ghostbusters' refrain followed by lots of shhhing. They come into view, moving cautiously and quietly with their 'Ghostbusting machine'. Rowena carries a bed-bottle.

James	What's that for?
Rowena	We can put the ghost in it.
Darren	Poor ghost.

The ghostbusters near the boiler-room door. They are becoming genuinely frightened, except for Darren who is not going to show it even if he feels it. James whispers.

James	Make sure 'e doesn't slime you.
Lucy	Urrh!

Rowena is having second thoughts.

Rowena	Maybe Nurse Mags was wrong.
Darren	You're scared.
Darren	Supposing there is a ghost?

They all hesitate. The corridor and shadows now take on a much more eerie quality.

Darren	There's no such things.
James	There is.
Darren	Only on films.
James	No, there is – specially in an old place like this.

Darren	Souls of restless spirits . . .
James	. . . looking for revenge . . .
Lucy	I'm frightened.

Darren is still not about to admit he is.

Darren	Maybe, we should take Lucy back . . . come another time.

Rowena's frightened eyes look left and right.

Rowena	Perhaps the Ghost of South Park is watching us now . . . I've gone all cold . . .
James	So have I . . .

Suddenly a loud grating sound followed by a hiss emanates from the boiler room. Panic stations – they flee back to the ward.

Scene 18 *(Internal): Children's ward*

Cal lies back in bed looking at the ceiling.

Bryony	Cal . . .
Cal	You don't want to go Ghostbusting an'all do you?
Bryony	I've had enough excitement for one day.
Cal	I'm sorry I got you in trouble with your old feller.
Bryony	It wasn't your fault . . .
	They have to spoil everything.
Cal	Still – you might have got hurt.
Bryony	I knew I'd be all right. I trusted you.
Cal	Don't tell anyone – bad for my image . . .
Bryony	Thanks anyway.
Cal	I'll tell you what. I'll take you out in your wheelchair again. You know, for a proper walk, out in the grounds . . .
Bryony	Yes, I'd like that.
Cal	If they let us . . .
Bryony	D'you think Sister Meadows was really annoyed?
Cal	Na . . . She's . . .

The calm is shattered by the return of the terrified ghostbusters who burst in and scurry to their beds.

Rowena Is it following us?

Cal . . . Will you lot belt up.

Rowena That ghost came after us.

Cal I'll come after you if you don't keep quiet.

Lucy Will you look after us, Cal?

Cal Yeah . . .

Lucy Thanks.

Cal As long as you keep quiet.

Scene 19 *(Internal): Boiler-room corridor*

A discarded wheelchair and vaccum cleaner are outside the boiler-room door. The door opens slowly. A maintenance man with spanners, etc. emerges, wiping his hands on an oily rag. He is puzzled to see the 'Ghostbusting machine' but he just wants to get home for his cocoa.

Scene 20 *(Internal): Children's ward*

The next day Nurse Mags gives Danny his breakfast.

Nurse Mags D'you sleep well?

Darren All right.

Cal I'm glad you did – all the noise some people were making.

James There's a ghost in this hospital isn't there, Nurse Mags?

Nurse Mags is joking.

Nurse Mags There must be . . .

The younger ones look horrified.

Nurse Mags . . . because it left the vacuum in the middle of the corridor by the boiler room.

The younger ones look guilty.

Nurse Mags	. . . Only a ghost could have done that, couldn't it?

Rowena and Lucy share a look.

Scene 21 *(Internal): Baby ward*

Dr Gallagher holds Hannah as he talks to her.

Dr Gallagher	So, you've come to see your little brother?
Hannah	Yes.
Dr Gallagher	Well, he's doing very, very well.

Dr Gallagher puts Hannah down and she stays near Mrs Bevans, who is seated. Hannah delves into Mrs Bevans' bag.

Mrs Bevans	Dr Woods says Jack's on the mend.
Dr Gallagher	Yeah, he's past the tricky time, when infections can complicate matters.

Hannah is playing with some nail varnish. She is unscrewing the top.

Dr Gallagher	You'll soon be home together.
Mrs Bevans	It's funny, I felt dead strange here when I came in with Jack – now I feel like part of the furniture.

Dr Gallagher sees what Hannah is doing.

Dr Gallagher	Hannah, don't do that.

Hannah has the nail varnish round her eyes. Mrs Bevans looks at Hannah.

Mrs Bevans	Hannah!

She goes to her.

Mrs Bevans	Not near your eyes.

Hannah panics, drops the nail varnish and covers her eyes. The varnish goes in her eyes and she screams. Dr Gallagher goes to her, easing Mrs Bevans out of the way. Dr Gallagher gently examines Hannah's eyes.

Dr Gallagher	Come on, let's see.

He speaks to Mrs Bevans.

Dr Gallagher	What is it?
Mrs Bevans	Nail varnish. Is she all right?

Dr Gallagher picks Hannah up.

Dr Gallagher	I'll get her down to ophthalmics.

He hurries out.

Dr Gallagher	Bring the bottle, they might need to see what it is.

Mrs Bevans picks up the bottle and hurries after him.

Scene 22 *(Internal): Lee Jones' bedroom*

Lee is in bed, covers pulled up. He is awake as Mrs Jones brings a cup of tea.

Mrs Jones	I bet it was nice to be in your own bed again.
Lee	Yeah, brilliant.

He sees the tea.

Lee	Tea in bed as well?

He takes it. Mrs Jones jokes.

Mrs Jones	Don't get used to it – You can bring me one tomorrow.
Lee	It's a deal.
Mrs Jones	Are you having a lie-in?
Lee	Nah, I've been in bed too much these last few weeks.
Mrs Jones	Right I'll do your breakfast then.
Lee	Ta.

Mrs Jones goes out. Lee gets out of bed. He goes to a chest of drawers which he opens. In it we see three neatly folded football kits. One Manchester United, one England, and one his school team. He takes this out, smooths it, then, realising the implications of the no-football rule, slings it to one side.

Scene 23 *(Internal): Mrs Jones' kitchen*

Lee is in a tracksuit and trainers. He finishes his breakfast. Mrs Jones wipes the working surface. On the wall there is a diet sheet.

Mrs Jones It's good to have you back home – I've missed you.

Lee gives an embarrassed smile.

Lee Shurrup, Mam.

Mrs Jones See. I've pinned your diet sheet up – I'm getting organised.

Lee You'll be making me use a bed-bottle next.

Mrs Jones Like they said, if you look after yourself and don't do anything daft, you can still lead a good life.

Lee I know . . .

He stands.

Lee I'm going down to the match in a bit.

Mrs Jones gives him a look. Lee quickly adds.

Lee Just to watch.

Mrs Jones Well, don't even think about kicking a ball.

Lee No, course not.

As Mrs Jones clears the table, we hear a knock at the front door. Lee gets up quickly to answer it.

Lee That'll be Ben. I'll see you later, Mam.

Mrs Jones See you.

She calls after him.

Mrs Jones Don't bang your arm. Don't get cold.

Lee jokes back to her.

Lee I'll try and enjoy myself too.

Lee opens the door to Ben, who has got a sports bag.

Ben Hiya. You all set?

Lee Yes.

Mrs Jones comes through to see them off, drying her hands.

Mrs Jones   See you lads. Good luck with the match, Ben.

Ben   We'll paste 'em.

Mrs Jones watches Ben and Lee go – pleased Lee is back home and able to get out.

Scene 24 *(Internal): Ophthalmics*

Hannah's eyes are being examined by an ophthalmologist using a slit lamp (which looks like binoculars on a stand). Mrs Bevans reassures Hannah gently as the examination finishes. Dr Gallagher looks on.

Mrs Bevans   That's a good girl, Hannah – nearly finished.

The ophthalmologist smiles at Hannah and Mrs Bevans and goes over to speak to Dr Gallagher in background.

Hannah   Can I go and see Jack now?

Mrs Bevans   We'll see.

She looks at Dr Gallagher and the ophthalmologist. Dr Gallagher speaks to the ophthalmologist.

Dr Gallagher   Yes, thanks.

He smiles at Mrs Bevans.

Dr Gallagher   Right, Hannah, let's go back to the children's ward.

Scene 25 *(Internal): Sluice room*

Nurse Mags is emptying a washer. Sister Meadows enters.

Sister Meadows   Oh, Nurse Mags, could you make a bed up for Hannah?

Nurse Mags   Of course. Her eyes all right?

Sister Meadows   Ophthalmics thinks she's OK, but want to keep her in overnight, just to be sure.

Nurse Mags   Poor Mrs Bevans, she's got her hands full one
                    way and another.

Sister Meadows Hasn't she just.

Scene 26 *(Internal): Dayroom*

*Mrs Bevans sits alone in the dayroom, deep in
thought. Dr Gallagher, passing, sees her and comes
in.*

Dr Gallagher   Penny for them.

Mrs Bevans   Just thinking . . .

Dr Gallagher   No permanent damage . . .

Mrs Bevans   . . . Thinking how flipping useless I am. How
                    could I sit there while she played with that
                    bottle. . . . She might have been blinded.

                    *Dr Gallagher sits. He touches Mrs Bevans' arm
                    reassuringly.*

Dr Gallagher   Ey, come on, she's all right. Four year olds get
                    into all sorts of things.

Scene 27 *(External): Sports field.*

*Some players from both teams are already in kit
having a kick-about. Ben is in his kit with Lee who
cannot resist knocking the ball about.*

Mr Starkey   Smashing to see you back, Lee.

Lee   You need me out on the Park, Coach.

Mr Starkey   Sure – but I want to know you're properly fit.
                    Today you're a spectator.

Lee   But I am fit, Mr Starkey.

Mr Starkey   Sorry, mate, the team's been picked.

                    He looks at his watch.

Mr Starkey   Right, lads, let's have you out now . . .

                    *Mr Harries, the referee, runs over from the
                    dressing room.*

Mr Harries   Just had a call; one of your lads has got the 'flu–

goalie . . . Farmer . . .

Mr Starkey I'm sure he's done this to wind me up.

Ben goes over to join them.

Ben What's the problem?

Mr Starkey No goalie, that's all!

Mr Starkey follows Ben's gaze to Lee. Just a moment's thought. But we know Lee cannot resist – it is destiny!

Lee I'll play, sir.

Mr Starkey You're not fit.

Lee I'm not daft enough to play if I wasn't. It's no different being in goal than standing here.

Mr Starkey hesitates.

Mr Starkey Are you sure?

Lee Course – I can play in these, sir.

He indicates his tracksuit – he's already moving off. Mr Harries and Mr Starkey look at each other.

Mr Harries Come on, we're late starting as it is.

He blows the whistle and shouts.

Mr Harries Captains, please.

In the background we see Lee being greeted by his team mates. Mr Starkey's expression shows he has some misgivings.

Scene 28 *(External): Sports field.*

We see Lee in goal, concentrating on play.

Lee shouts.

Lee Right reds come on, come on, tackle him, get stuck in . . . don't stand and watch them.

Whistle blows.

Lee Come on, Ref. That was never a foul – how much they paying you?

We see Mr Harries has blown for a free kick near

Lee's penalty area. Mr Harries comes over to Lee.

Mr Harries   Any more of your lip, Jones, and you're off.

Ben calls over to Lee.

Ben   Shortest come-back in history.

Lee   Sorry Ref.

Mr Harries shouts to the others.

Mr Harries   Come on, free kick.

They get ready to take a free kick. We see Lee preparing to save. Mr Harries' whistle blows and we see Lee dive and make a spectacular save. He grasps the ball, stands hugging it, a look of real satisfaction on his face.

Lee places the ball for a goal kick. He walks back and turns to face it. He looks to see where his players are and gives it an almighty boot up the field. He watches it, then turns to come back to the goal. Suddenly he staggers, clutches his side and collapses.

Questions and Explorations

Episode One

Discussion

1 How does the episode grab the viewer's attention? How does it keep you interested until the end of the episode?

2 How can you tell that the writing is for television? Think about the descriptions of the settings and action, the number of scenes and where they are set. Could this script be performed on stage?

3 What do we learn about Lee in this first episode?

4 Describe Lee's medical condition.

5 What are our first impressions of Danny? What appears to be the matter with him?

6 Why did Nurse Miller hit Danny? What will happen to Nurse Miller?

7 Cal enters and tells James that there is nothing wrong with him. So why is he on children's ward?

8 The first episode shows different types of hospital discipline. What are they?

9 How should Nurse Grahams dress? Why?

Writing

10 There is clearly a great deal of strain on the ward. Write a diary of events for this day. Add events of your own if you wish.

11 When the writers write the script, they follow a storyline for the episode which has been drawn up and agreed beforehand. Read the storyline for Episode One (on page 168).

a) How is it different from the script?

b) Why do you think this is?

c) Would you have scripted any part of this storyline differently?

Drama

12 How do we know that the staff are divided in their views about what to do with Danny? Who holds what view?

Take roles as different members of staff and improvise the meeting where you discuss what to do with Danny.

13 Improvise what happens between Cal combing his hair in the toilet and the next thing he remembers which is coming round in the ambulance.

14 A new patient joins the children's ward. In groups, decide who the newcomer is, and the reasons for his or her arrival. Think about the new patient's attitude to his or her illness and being in hospital and the reaction of other patients and members of staff.

Prepare and present one or two key scenes, for example, the patient's arrival or his or her first encounter with another patient or staff member.

Episode Two

Discussion

1 Who does the main focus shift to in this episode?

2 Danny's parents says he is 'just highly spirited'. Why do you think they say that? Do you agree with them?

3 What is the evidence so far on what is actually wrong with Danny?

4 Why does Lee say 'I don't have a brother' rather than 'no'?

5 What is the dramatic effect of introducing Lee's brother Marcus, at the end of the episode instead of earlier on?

6 Why does Lee's mother cry?

7 Why did Lee's parents separate? Is it important to know all the background information to these characters?

8 Why do we have the tortoise and the game of Trivial Pursuit in this episode? What do they do for the mood of the episode?

9 What does Lee mean by 'Might as well be dead then'?

Writing

10 The episode deals with the dangers of fireworks. Write up as a newspaper report the story of how Philip got burnt.

11 Write some case notes for Danny from evidence in Episode Two. These can go back several years and involve changes of address and schools.

12 Bryony celebrates her fourteenth birthday on the children's

ward. Write a letter from her to a friend who sent her a card describing what it is like on the ward from her point of view.

Drama

13 Dr Woods tells Lee's mother that he will not be able to play football again and she then has to tell Lee. Improvise a scene where you have to receive and pass on some bad news.

Episode Three

Discussion

1 This episode takes place on Bonfire Day. What other annual events would make a good background to the events in *Children's Ward*?

2 How do James, Darren and Bryony plan to confirm their suspicion that Cal is cheating at Trivial Pursuit? Is it right to teach Cal a lesson in this way?

3 Why do you think Cal is so reluctant to tell Dr Kahn about his symptoms?

4 How does Jack the trolleyman find out the information he wants from Philip?

5 The atmosphere on the ward seems more relaxed than in the first two episodes. How does the writer show this?

6 Danny's behaviour has not improved. What is the food allergy specialist going to do?

7 Mrs Phillips enters the office to make a complaint. What is it?

8 Why do we have rules about the sale of fireworks? What action would you have taken in Jack's position?

9 Why is the Trivial Pursuit match played in the boiler room and not on the ward?

10 What effect is the final scene intended to have on the viewers?

Writing

11 Read the character description of Cal at the start of the book. Think about what we know about him from this episode. Then write an end-of-term school report for him.

12 Write Danny's diet book for a couple of days. How do certain foods make you feel? Do they have an effect on your moods?

13 What impression have you formed of Nurse Grahams since she joined as a student nurse in Episode One. Write the report which Sister Meadows might submit on her at the end of her first two weeks.

Drama

14 'I've got you. . .'

In groups, explore the following situation:

One person has gained a great deal of power over another perhaps through a fear, blackmail or other means. He or she could be a bully or a nurse or a teacher or gangland leader, or someone like Cal. Plan three or four scenes which show why that person wants power, how they get it and whether their plans come unstuck.

Decide:

a) what kind of power the person has

b) how he/she uses it

c) what situations show this happening

d) how others react

Episode Four

Discussion

1 What does Cal discover about himself in this episode? How does he react? How does he imagine others will react to his condition?

2 Does anyone feel that it was wrong to teach Cal a lesson? Why?

3 Why has Danny's behaviour changed at the start of the episode?

   When Danny has been given the orange squash, why does he start throwing things? Why does he say 'what's funny' when he stops?

4 Why does Cal not want to use the wheelchair?

5 How does the relationship between Nurse Mitchell and Cal develop in this episode?

6 Who is Digger?

7 How will Cal's and Danny's lives change after leaving the children's ward?

8 How does the writer include humour in this episode?

9 What is the difference between the parents of Cal, Lee and Danny?

Writing

10 Bryony says 'This place. It's all right when you know the routine. But it must do their heads in when they don't want to be here.'

Choose two characters that appear in this episode – one who 'knows the routine' and another who does not want to be in hospital – and write the letters they might send to friends describing hospital and what they think of it.

11 Write Digger's diary of a day at school.

12 Write a story about an emergency, illness or accident which has happened to you. Explain how it happened, and how you and the people around you felt. Were you treated differently afterwards? Did the incident change you? Did it change the way you saw other people?

13 Write a file about Cal's epilepsy, from his first admission to the ward and everything that has happened to him.

Drama

14 Improvise Cal's first day back at school after leaving the children's ward. How do his friends react to him. What does he tell them?

Episode Five

Discussion

1 How is this episode different from the ones that have

preceded it? Think about what happens during it. What is the 'mood' of the whole episode?

2 Why does Lee play football on the ward?

3 Why does Danny row with Cal?

4 Why does Cal trust Nurse Mitchell?

5 What is Lee warned about in this episode? Does the scene at the end of the episode suggest that he is going to take notice of the warning?

6 Why do the writers have a character like Jack Crossley in the series?

7 Why don't Cal's mates visit him?

Writing

8 Write a number of requests for the hospital radio programme which reflect Rowena's description of people on the ward, and ask for a suitable choice of record.

Drama

9 Improvise the scene which took place between Student Nurse Grahams and Sister Meadows before we see Nurse Grahams washing her hair.

10 What happens when Rowena returns to the ward after her DJ act? Think about what her attitude will be and the likely reactions of the other children, then improvise her entrance to the ward.

Episode Six

Discussion

1 What must Lee remember to do to remain healthy?

2 Why is it easier to do the 'wheelie run' on television than on stage?

3 Why does Cal say 'if they let us' when talking to Bryony?

4 Do you think Cal was right to take Bryony on a 'wheelie run'?

5 What do Bryony's parents think about the children's ward?

6 What does Nurse Mitchell mean by 'talk about them and us'?

7 Why do the kids go ghostbusting?

8 Do you believe Lee when he says, 'I'm not bitter, I don't care about them, that's all'?

9 Episode Six ends as Episode One began. Why is the second emergency going to be more significant than the first?

Writing

11 Write a ghost story called 'Midnight at Sparkies'.

12 Write a story plan for Episode Seven predicting what you think might happen as a result of the events in the final scenes of Episode Six.

Drama

13 Improvise the scene which took place when Sister Meadows 'read the Riot Act' to Cal and Bryony about the 'wheelie run'. Think particularly about how both Cal and Bryony react to this, and what they say.

14 Improvise a scene where individuals from different backgrounds meet and become friends like Cal and Bryony. How do their parents and friends react to the match?

All Episodes

Discussion

1 If you have ever been to a hospital, can you remember your first visit? How did you feel before going? Were you confident or nervous? Is it in any way like a first day at school?

2 What advice would you give to a younger brother or sister going into hospital?

3 Which are your favourite characters in the series? Why?

4 Do you find all the characters in *Children's Ward* convincing? Say who you find particularly believable or unbelievable and explain why.

5 If you were the producer of *Children's Ward*, what topics, events or illnesses would you want it to cover?

6 Are there any you would not want it to cover?

7 What problems and advantages does a television playwright have compared to a writer of plays for the theatre?

Writing

8 What would it be useful for new patients to know about the children's ward in advance? Write a set of 'rules' or a short guidebook that will help them to settle in well.

9 Write about a day in the life of Dr Woods, the head of children's ward. It can be either in diary form or a short story.

10 When Lee leaves hospital in the last episode he says 'I'm over the moon to be on me way.' Describe how you have felt when you have left somewhere you have been for a long time. It might be coming home after a long stay in hospital, or leaving one school to go to another, or moving house.

11 *Children's Ward* tries to use natural, vivid dialogue suited to its characters. Choose something you have seen recently or are about to see – television, radio or stage play, a film or an episode of a series – and make notes on the following questions:

a) If the characters were real people would they speak as they do in the script, for example, would they know (and choose to use) the words the playwright or scriptwriter has given them to say?

b) Do the various characters sound like themselves, or are they actually speaking with the dramatist's own voice all the time?

12 Now write one or two extra scenes for one of the episodes in this book. For example, a cafeteria scene or a scene in the boiler room. Make it clear where this scene appears in the episode involved. Remember to make the dialogue appropriate for the characters and that setting and action are as important in television scripts as dialogue.

13 Plan the characters and write two or three storylines for a new TV series. It could be based on your school or somewhere else in the neighbourhood.

14 Imagine that you are going to direct an episode of *Children's Ward* and write director's notes for it. What studio settings would you need? Do you need to shoot scenes on location? How should the characters be dressed? What 'props' will you need? Are you going to use music anywhere in the production, and if so, what and where?

15 Write a letter to the *TV* or *Radio Times* about a programme you have seen recently which you have strong feelings about.

16 Collect reviews from newspapers on programmes you have seen. How fair do you feel they are? Write your own review of a programme or play you have seen recently.

Drama

15 Compile and present your own trailer for *Children's Ward* which will make viewers want to see the episodes in this book. Discuss and choose the clips you will include and then act them out.

16 Improvise one of the following:

a) a family disagreement about what television programmes to watch. Start your dialogue a few minutes before the programmes are about to begin. You can either base it on your own family or invent a fictional family.

b) a family receives news that one of the children has been in an accident and rushed into hospital.

c) You are walking along a street and someone asks you the

way to a particular newsagents. Your companion disagrees with your directions.

Think carefully before you start about what sort of character you are and how you would speak.

17 Act out a scene in which an experienced nurse gives advice to a new recruit on how to handle a difficult patient.

Storyline for Episode One

Lee

On the football pitch Lee is playing centre forward. We see just what a good player he is – it looks like a goal is in the offing when Lee collapses to the ground. Lee's friend, Ben, goes to his aid; thinks somebody must have kicked him. The opposite side shout 'scam', but the games teacher/referee sees that Lee is genuinely ill; he shouts to Ben to call for an ambulance.

Ambulance is racing through the streets with siren going and blue light flashing.

Lee is wheeled down the corridor in to the emergency examination room.

Lee's mother, Carol, chasing down the corridor.

Theatre is prepared for emergency operation. Carol in, she is shocked to see her son so ill. She is told Lee's condition is serious – he must have been ignoring severe pains for quite a while; they have to do an emergency operation to remove an infected and bleeding kidney – it is a life and death situation. Mrs Jones is asked if there is any other family besides herself. She says no, and signs for her son's kidney to be removed.

Lee is taken down to theatre for the operation.

Carol sits alone waiting for her son's operation to be over.

Lee pulls through the operation and he is moved onto the renal intensive care unit where he is placed on a dialysis machine. Mrs Jones is by his side.

Danny

(Sub-plot to this story should introduce new Student Nurse Grahams and Nurse Miller's leaving.)

We should come in hard on Danny. We will him hear before we see him. The plaster room is near the examination room or where Lee's mother is waiting (depending on where it comes in the story).

Fresh from having his leg plastered, we see the culprit of that loud mouth as he is wheeled along the corridor heading for the children's ward, shouting – he's not staying in some stupid bed! He's going home.

It takes Nurse Miller, Nurse Grahams and Nurse Mags to get Danny into bed. He resists all the way, landing Nurse Miller a blow to his jaw. Nurse Miller instinctively hits Danny back. Nurse Mitchell's beady eye catches it all, and she is off to make her report.

Danny is finally tractioned. Sister Meadows finds Nurse Miller beside himself with shame. He had only a week left on the children's ward before he moves to women's medical and he has really blotted his copy book. He tells Sister Meadows he is upset to be leaving the children's ward, and he feels like a complete idiot in front of Nurse Grahams.

Within half an hour of being secured on to traction, Danny frees himself and hurls himself out of the bed, fracturing the brand new plaster cast. Sister Meadows thinks he is going to be impossible and tells Dr Gallagher and Dr Woods she wants him off her ward. He is obviously a psychological case. Dr Woods says that he has a medical condition – broken femur, and they have to treat him. Sister Meadows is irked.

Danny is practically forced into a wheelchair and pushed along the corridor back to have his plaster repaired. He puts his good foot on the floor and brings the wheelchair to an abrupt stop. The wheelchair jars into Sister Meadows stomach and it winds her – that's it, she's had enough! He's only been on the ward an hour and a half and he's caused total chaos. Dr Gallagher tries some stern talking and pushes him down to the plaster room.

Danny back from having his plaster repaired. He is about to throw another tantrum as he is lifted back on the bed. Nurse Grahams wonders why they don't lift the mattress off the bed and lay him on the floor – flat.

We leave Danny's story with Danny laid on the floor, his leg set in a splint and glimmer of respect from Danny towards Nurse Grahams.

In the sluice room. Nurse Mags trying to console Nurse Miller – 'Don't walk out, do your test and try and forget about it'. Nurse Miller says he'll have the fact that he hit a patient on his records for the rest of his career. Nurse Mags reminds him that Nurse Mitchell has things on her records and that doesn't stop her from bossing people around. Nurse Miller tells Nurse Mags he just wants to be a good nurse.

A quiet word from Sister Meadows to Nurse Grahams. Could she wear normal coloured tights tomorrow, not green, and she'd appreciate it if she had a word with Nurse Miller.

Dr Woods thinks – it's obvious Danny's a disturbed child with little if no parental control. Sister Meadows thinks – he's a child with a psychological problem; he should be on a psychiatric ward.

Nurse Grahams and Nurse Miller go off duty together, friends. He is going to do his test next week.

Hopefully a resolution story with a cliffhanger. End episode as Nurse Grahams and Nurse Miller pass the paediatric renal unit where Mrs Jones sits next to her sleeping son who is on a dialysis machine.

Other patients included in Episode One are:

Cal

He is admitted for observation, but he is not forthcoming about his medical condition.

Bryony

A fourteen-year-old girl, suffering the effects of chronic rheumatoid arthritis. A long-term case, primarily in need of bed rest and a lot of psychological support to see her through a rough period. She is a static observer of the ward and its idiosyncrasies. She watches Cal play James and then Darren at Trivial Pursuit. He wins hands down. By the end of the episode we know that Cal is in for observation – he has suspected epilepsy.

Lucy

Lucy is admitted from Casualty with minor scalding to her legs from an accident involving a boiling teapot (cautionary tale as much as we want to play it).

She doesn't settle easily, wants to be home. Her mother is invited to bed down in the parents' quarters. This gives Lucy some comfort, but she doesn't take to the other kids much. She is a bit of a loner.

She sucks a dummy, and Nurse Mags tries to persuade her to abandon the device . . . to no avail.

Her story will tick over during the following episodes, sometimes coming to the foreground, sometimes remaining in the background. Occasionally she will be unseen throughout an episode.

Set Plans

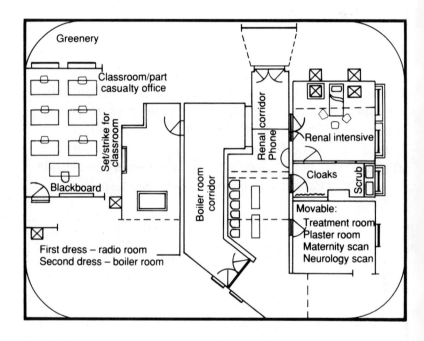

Greenery

Classroom/part casualty office

Set/strike for classroom

Blackboard

First dress – radio room
Second dress – boiler room

Boiler room corridor

Renal corridor
Phone

Renal intensive

Cloaks

Scrub

Movable:
Treatment room
Plaster room
Maternity scan
Neurology scan

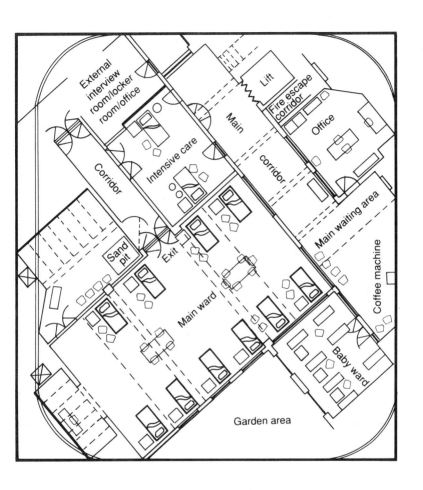

External
interview
room/locker
room/office

Corridor

Intensive care

Main

Lift

Fire escape
corridor

Office

corridor

Main waiting area

Coffee machine

Sand
pit

Exit

Main ward

Baby ward

Garden area

Glossary

aggro	aggravation
allergy	sensitivity to certain substances, eg foods, pollens, insect bites
American Tan	a colour of women's tights
artery	blood vessel carrying fresh blood from the lungs and heart to the body
barium enema	a form of X-ray where an opaque solution is sent through the lower bowel
bommies	bonfires
boycott	refusal to buy goods in order to punish the sellers or persuade them to do something
clips	sometimes used instead of stitches to repair a wound
colic	severe gripping pains in the stomach
consultant	senior medical specialist
dialysis machine	specialised machine used for cleaning the blood when the kidneys have stopped working
drip	feeding solution attached to a patient
EEG	electroencephalogram – a record of electrical activity in the brain
electrodes	pods placed on the skin to detect body activity
fistula	surgically made, pipe-like, body passage
glucose	a form of sugar found in fruit juice and blood
Grand Mal convulsion	a major epileptic seizure
Grand National	annual horse race
gremlin	word used to describe the cause of a problem
haemodialysis	cleaning the blood using a dialysis machine

hydrotherapy	treatment of certain illnesses by swimming and other exercises in water
hyperactivity	persistent fits of restlessness
infusion	feeding solution attached to patient by a drip
intussusception	a condition in small children where the lower bowel folds inside itself
lacerations	cuts and grazes
Maine Road	football ground where Manchester United play
migraine	severe headaches often caused by bright lights and allergies
neurological	dealing with the body's nervous system
Nigel Mansell	racing car driver
Opthalmics	a branch of medicine dealing with the study and treatment of the eyes
Pac-man	a portable video game
phial of blood	sample of blood for testing
physiotherapist	someone who improves bodily movement
pot	plaster cast
psychedelic	brightly multicoloured
psychiatric	a branch of medicine dealing with the treatment of mental disorders
pyrotechnics	fireworks
radiologist	someone who takes and reads X-rays
recovery position	First Aid position used to prevent a patient choking
renal artery	main blood vessel serving the kidney
Renal Unit	ward dealing specifically with kidney patients
Round Table	a social group which raises money and provides help to local charities
saline	salt solution which helps to balance the body fluids
schtumm	quiet

Scouse	from Liverpool
seizure	sudden attack or fit, leading to inability to feel or move
sluice room	place where ward instruments are cleaned and sterilised
solvent abuse	glue sniffing
Sparkies	affectionate nickname for South Park Hospital
sputum cup	vessel for carrying samples of phlegm
sterile	free from germs
stethoscope	instrument for listening to the body's internal activities
stools	evacuation of the bowels
subclavian line	line entering the subclavian artery (lying under the collar bone)
Tartrazine	orange colouring present in foods, particularly orange squash
temporal lobe	a condition affecting the brain and nervous system where
epilepsy	patients suffer seizures
theatre	operating room
toxic wastes	products manufactured by the body which can be harmful if the kidneys cannot dispose of them.
trauma	a painful event which can take a long time to recover from
tulle gras dressing	fine bandage used for dressing burns
tumour	a growth in the body which may be dangerous, eg cancer
ultrasound scan	similar to an X-ray but using ultrasound to check for internal bodily disorders. Also used to check on pregnancies
vein	blood vessel carrying used blood back to the heart and lungs